Newnes Short Wave Listening]

Newnes Short Wave Listening Handbook

Joe Pritchard, G1UQW

Heinemann Newnes

Heinemann Newnes
An imprint of Heinemann Professional Publishing
Halley Court, Jordan Hill, Oxford OX2 8EJ

OXFORD   LONDON   MELBOURNE   AUCKLAND   SINGAPORE
IBADAN   NAIROBI   GABORONE   KINGSTON

First published 1989

British Library Cataloguing in Publication Data

Pritchard, Joe
    Newnes shortwave listening handbook.
    1. Amateur radio equipment
    I. Title
    621.3841'51

    ISBN 0–434–91550–5

Printed in Great Britain by
Redwood Burn Ltd, Trowbridge
Typeset by August Filmsetting, Haydock, St Helens

Contents

Preface

When I was about 10 years old, I contracted the 'bug' of SWLing –
Short Wave Listening. By tuning away from Radio 2, I found that
there were many other stations, some from the other side of the world,
that could be heard. I learnt that the signals heard depended on the
time of day at which I was listening, and also the season. After a while, I
became thoroughly hooked and started building simple receivers and
saving my pennies for a 'real' short wave (SW) radio. Once I had that, I
discovered the importance of a good aerial and began listening to
amateur radio operators and other signals that my simple radio sets
had been unable to receive.

That is how I got involved in short wave radio listening, a hobby
that has been surprisingly slow to catch on in Britain but that is quite
popular in other parts of the world. The aim of this book is to provide a
newcomer with enough information to get started in the hobby, and to
build his or her own receivers if so interested. Chapters 1 to 10 deal with
the technical side of radio reception, and the rest of the book deals with
listening techniques. What I have tried to do is to write the book that I
wished I had when I started 16 years ago – I hope that you find it useful.

Even when only one name appears on the jacket, a book is a team
effort. I would like to thank my publisher, Peter Dixon, for getting this
project off the ground and his patience in waiting for it to be finished. I
would also like to thank my parents who, over the years, put up with
having large amounts of wire strung around bedrooms and gardens
when I was constructing aerials. Finally, thanks to my wife, Nicky, for
putting up with an anti-social husband during the writing of the book
and who has now succumbed to the radio bug, as has our cat, who

loves sitting on log books when I am trying to write down details of a new station ....

73s and *Good DX*,
Joe Pritchard, G1UQW
Sheffield 1988

ONE

Some electrical principles

Possibly the greatest effects of technology on our lives have been caused by the science of electronics. It is responsible for the growth of global communications, computers and a host of other devices and systems that we use in our day-to-day lives. Most importantly for the purposes of this book, without it short wave radio would not exist and the airwaves would be as silent as they were before Marconi sent his famous messages. To start this book, I would like to explore some areas of electronics that are of importance to us. In Appendix 3 you will find several titles which will give a more in-depth study, so that you can take the topics covered here further should you wish.

Conductors and insulators

All matter is made of atoms, which for our purposes can be treated as the smallest whole particle of an element. An atom can be viewed as a small nucleus possessing a positive charge, surrounded by electrons which carry a negative electrical charge to render the atom electrically neutral. Elements can combine to form other materials, an example being common salt, where the metal sodium and the gas chlorine react together to form crystals of salt, a compound of the two elements. Some materials have atoms with electrons that are mobile and can move from atom to atom in a block of that substance – these materials are called *conductors* and include copper, iron, carbon and tin. Other materials exist where the electrons are more rigidly bound to the atoms that make up the material, be it an element or a compound. These substances are called *insulators*, and include rubber and plastics.

The movement of electrons in a conductor is a random affair until we organise it by forcing the electrons to drift one way or another in a

1

conductor. This movement of electrons through a conductor is called an *electric current*, and is caused by applying a *voltage* across the conductor, often from a battery (Figure 1.1). The battery is able to produce a supply of electrons by chemical action, and these electrons enter the conductor from the negative terminal of the battery and replace those that have drifted out of the other end of the conductor back into the positive terminal of the battery. The network of conductors linking the two terminals of the battery is called a *circuit*. However, conventionally, electric current is said to flow from *positive* to *negative*. The direction of flow of current was guessed at before the mechanism of electron movement was discovered, and, as is often the case, we got it wrong!

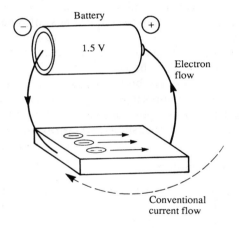

Figure 1.1

Conductors are usually formed into wires, often covered in insulating material such as plastic, cotton, enamel or rubber to prevent two adjacent wires touching each other. All conductors at room temperature exhibit some degree of opposition to the flow of current through it. This is called *resistance*.

Volts, amps and ohms

Current flow is measured in *amperes*, often abbreviated to *amps* (A) and is based on the number of electrons flowing through a particular point in the circuit per second. A current of about $6E+18$ electrons per second is 1 A. This is quite a lot of current for our purposes, and in modern electronics you will see currents quoted in terms of milliamps (mA, thousandths of an amp) or microamps (μA, millionths of an amp).

Voltage across circuits is measured in *volts* (V) and is a measure of the electromotive force (EMF) which drives electrons through circuits. When we are measuring voltage, it is usually measured with respect to a point in the circuit referred to as *ground* or *earth* (0V). All other voltages in the circuit are referred to as being positive or negative with respect to that point in the circuit.

Resistance to current flow is measured in units called *ohms* (Ω or R), nd the ohm is defined in terms of the volt and the amp. A circuit has a resistance of 1 Ω if a voltage of 1 V produces a current of 1 A. This is called *Ohm's law*, and is quite an important statement. Mathematically, it can be written:

$$V=IR \text{ or } R=V/I \text{ or } I=V/R$$

Some materials have a much higher resistance than others; carbon, for example, has a greater resistance than copper or silver. Circuit components can be made of these highly resistive materials so that we can put resistance into circuits whenever we please. These are called *resistors*. Resistance in a circuit has some interesting effects upon the circuit. For example, we can use resistance to change the voltage at different parts of the circuit (Figure 1.2). The total resistance offered to current is 20 Ω, and this results in a current of 0.075 A flowing around the circuit. To

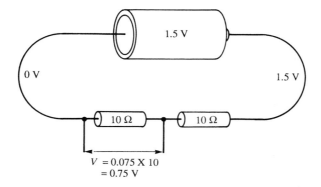

Figure 1.2

work out the voltage at the point between the two resistors, we simply look at the resistance between that point and 0 V (10 R) and the current flow (0.075 A) and use V = IR. This shows a voltage of 0.75 V.

This is a rather idealised view of things, because the battery used will also exhibit some resistance, called *internal resistance*, and so the EMF of the battery (in this case 1.5 V), has to drive current through the 20 Ω resistance in the circuit *and* through the internal resistance of the battery itself. This usually causes some loss of EMF, the battery acting like another resistance in the circuit as well as a power source. The best battery has a low internal resistance and as batteries get old and wear out, their internal resistance rises.

Power

When a current flows through conductors, some energy is lost due to the resistance of the circuit. This is lost as heat, the conductors warming up as the current flows through it. In extreme cases, with a high current and a relatively high resistance, conductors with a low melting point will melt. This is the basis of the fuse. If the conductor is suspended in a vacuum, and is of relatively high melting point, the conductor will glow and give off light when current passes through it – the light bulb. In each case, power is said to be *dissipated* by the circuit, is measured in *watts* and is calculated as:

$$P = VI \text{ or } P = I^2 R$$

DC and AC voltages

In the examples so far, the voltage provided by the battery has been such that the positive terminal always acts to 'attract' the drifting electrons and the negative terminal acts to 'push' electrons into the circuit. The voltage at various points in the circuit will be constant relative to 0 V, and such a circuit is called a *direct current*, or DC, circuit.

However, there are circuits where the voltage at points within the circuit is constantly changing – at one instant a point may be positive with respect to 0 V and an instant later it may be negative with respect to 0 V! Such a circuit is called an *alternating current* (AC) circuit, and such circuits form the basis of all our communications systems as well as the National Grid by which power is distributed to our homes. The most common form an AC voltage takes is the sinewave, alternating around 0 V though other forms are possible (Figure 1.3). The number

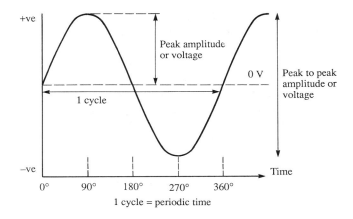

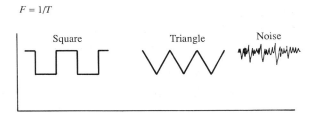

Figure 1.3

of cycles per second is called the *frequency* of the AC voltage, and can be obtained by:

$$F = 1/T$$

Frequency is measured in *hertz* (Hz) and 1 Hz is 1 cycle per second. Although the size of such a voltage at any given time is measured in volts, the position of that voltage with respect to time is measured in degrees from the start point of that particular cycle rather than in seconds or milliseconds. A full cycle is said to occupy 360°. The degree notation is also used when we are dealing with more than one alternating waveform in the same circuit. Look at Figure 1.4, where we have two alternating voltages, with the same frequency, but starting at different positions along their respective cycles. The numbers 1 to 4 indicate corresponding positions on each waveform, and the two are

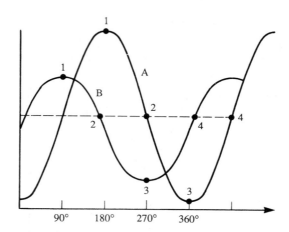

Figure 1.4

90° apart. They are said to be 90° *out of phase* with each other. If they had started at the same time, they would be *in phase* with one another. In this example, wave A can be said to *lead* wave B, which, in turn, can be called the *lagging* wave.

AC signals will interact with one another in circuits, to give rise to signals that may no longer be sinusoidal in shape. In addition, two sinusoidal waveforms can give rise to signals of totally different frequencies to those that were first present.

Ohm's law and AC

When we apply Ohm's law to a circuit containing a resistor and fed by AC, the voltage across the resistor and the current through it are found to be in phase with each other. In such calculations, it is common to use a value called the *instantaneous voltage* of the AC. This is the voltage present at a given instant in time. A further parameter, called the *root mean square* (RMS) value of an AC waveform, is also useful. This is about 0.707 times the peak voltage of an alternating voltage, and is equal to the DC voltage that would produce the same heating effect in a resistance as the AC voltage in question. This RMS value is only valid for a sinusoidal waveform.

We tend to measure frequencies in kilohertz (kHz) i.e., thousands of cycles per second, or megahertz (MHz) i.e., millions of cycles per second as well as hertz.

Capacitance and inductance

We have already seen that a conductor exhibits resistance; when we start using alternating voltages two more effects come in to play, called *capacitance* and *inductance*.

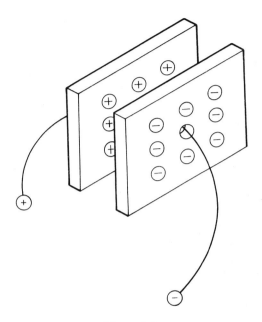

Figure 1.5

Figure 1.5 shows a couple of metal plates, quite close to each other, connected to a power source. This is a simple *capacitor*. Common sense tells us that no current will flow through the air gap in between the two plates. However, what will happen is that one plate will experience a deficit of electrons as they drift towards the positive side of the power supply whilst the other plate will experience a build up of electrons as more electrons are repelled from the negative supply side into the plate. In a very short time, this electron flow will stop and the plates will have an *electric field* between them, and if we were to remove the voltage the capacitor would be carrying an electric charge due to the presence of the electrons and would also have a voltage across it. The ratio of the charge to the voltage exhibited by a particular arrangement of conductors insulated from one another in this way is the *capacitance*, and is measured in units called *farads* (F). These are quite big units, and in electronics we use microfarads (μF) i.e., millionths of a farad, nanofarads (nf) i.e., thousand-millionths of a farad, and picofarads (pF) i.e., million millionths of a farad. Thus:

$$1 \, \mu F = 1000 \, nF = 1\,000\,000 \, pF$$

We have just seen that a DC voltage can be used to charge a capacitor up. The charging process occurs until the voltage across the capacitor plates is equal to that of the DC voltage charging it, and the time taken to do this depends upon the number of electrons flowing per second, i.e. the current, flowing into the capacitor. The time taken to charge a capacitor in a DC circuit thus depends upon the capacitance and the resistance of the circuit. The product of multiplying the capacitance of a circuit (in Farads) by the resistance of the circuit (in ohms) is called the *time constant* of a circuit. However, with an AC voltage a current can be seen to pass through the capacitor, as electrons flow into and out of the capacitor at each change of direction of the AC voltage. The larger the capacitance, the more current flows through. This current flow is also dependant upon frequency; this frequency dependant 'resistance' is called *reactance*, where:

$$X_c = 1/(6.28 \times f \times c)$$

where X_c is the reactance of a capacitor in ohms, f is the frequency in hertz, and C is the capacitance in farads. When AC is applied to a capacitor, current will flow through it but will lead the voltage by 90°. The current that will flow is given by:

$$I_c = V/X_c$$

An *inductor* is simply a coil of conducting wire (Figure 1.6a) which will pass a current when a voltage is applied to it. This causes a magnetic field, and an inductor acts like a magnet when current is flowing through it. When a current is first applied, the resulting magnetic field increases from zero to a maximum strength dependant upon the maximum current flowing through the wire, which in turn depends upon the resistance of the wire. Now, one of the effects of a changing magnetic field is to cause a voltage to be produced in any conductor within that magnetic field. In this case, the voltage produced in the wire will be in opposition to the voltage causing the current through the coil, and this will 'slow up' the rate at which current through the coil reaches a

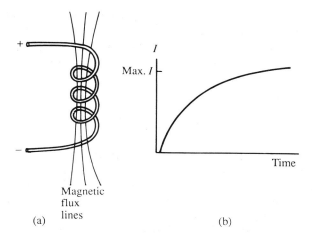

Figure 1.6

maximum value (Figure 1.6b). The *self-inductance* of a coil is a measure of the size of this 'slowing-up' factor, the higher the inductance is the longer it takes the current to reach its maximum value. This is measured in *henrys*, but in electronics we use millihenrys (mH) i.e. thousandths of a henry or microhenrys (μH) i.e. millionths of a henry. A coil has an inductance of 1 henry when a current changing at a rate of 1 amp per second causes a voltage across the coil of 1 volt.

A few moments' thought will lead to the realisation that if we apply AC across an inductor, then the inductor will exhibit resistance to the flow of current, as the magnetic field may not have allowed the current to reach its maximum value through the coil before the direction of the current changes. The current flow through an inductor lags the voltage by 90°, and inductive reactance is given by:

$$X_1 = 6.28 \times f \times L$$

where X_1 is the reactance, L is the inductance and f the frequency. The higher the frequency, the larger the reactance and so the smaller the current flow.

A changing current in one circuit can induce a voltage in a neighbouring circuit, especially if the two circuits are in the form of coils of wire in close proximity. The two coils are said to exhibit *mutual inductance*, and this is the basis of a component called the transformer. A changing current in one coil, called the primary coil, causes a changing voltage in the other coil, called the secondary. If we let V_p be the voltage across the primary, and V_s that across the secondary, and N_p and N_s the turns of wire on the primary and secondary coils respectively, then:

$$V_s/V_p = N_s/N_p$$

Transformers can thus be used to 'step up' i.e. increase or 'step down' i.e. decrease voltages or currents, as the current flowing in the secondary will be dependant upon the voltage induced and the resistance of the secondary coil. If the coils of wire are close together, then the coils are said to be tightly coupled, whereas if they are fairly far apart the coils are only loosely coupled. The looser the coupling, the less effect current flow through the primary will have on the secondary.

Impedance

All AC circuits exhibit resistance as well as inductance or capacitance, even if the resistance is just due to the wires of the circuit. The combination of the reactance and resistance is called the *impedance* of the circuit, and is given by:

$$Z = \sqrt{X^2 + R^2}$$

Impedance of circuits is quite important in electronics. If we have two circuits which need to be linked together, then the most efficient transfer of signals between the two circuits will occur when the impedance of the two circuits is the same. Impedance matching can be done in a variety of ways, the most popular being to use a transformer or a *network* – a collection of inductors, resistors or capacitors which will do the job.

Real components

Before looking at how we combine these components to make useful circuits, and examine the roles of more complex components in electronics, it's a good idea to examine real resistors, capacitors and inductors.

Figure 1.7 shows some typical resistors and the symbols that are

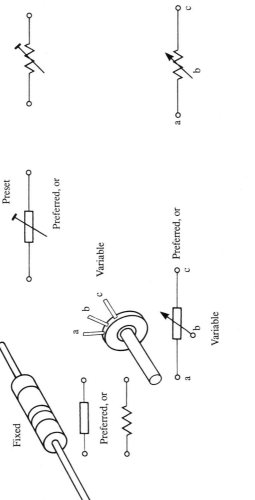

Figure 1.7

used to display them on circuit diagrams. The fixed resistor is the most common component in electronic circuitry, and is typically made of carbon or a special carbon film. The preset resistor is used in a circuit where it is necessary to provide some degree of variation of resistance, as may be needed when a circuit is being set up for the first time. The variable resistor, or potentiometer, is used when the adjustment of resistance is to be regularly carried out, for example, as in the volume control of a receiver. In variable resistors or presets, a track of carbon is used as the resistive element, with a moveable metal slider to 'tap off' the desired amount of resistance.

Fixed resistors do not usually have their values written on them in ohms, but have a series of coloured bands on them indicating their value. See Chapter 2 for details.

Figure 1.8 shows some typical capacitors. Rather than depend upon metal plates separated by air, the metal plates are separated from each other by thin layers of plastic (polyester capacitors) ceramic materials (ceramic capacitors), a chemical paste (electrolytic capacitors), mica sheets (trimmer capacitors) or air (variable capacitors). The type of capacitor used depends upon the type of AC signal that you are going to pass through them. For circuits with frequencies of a few hundred kilohertz upwards ceramic capacitors are often used, or other high quality types such as silver-mica capacitors. Polyester capacitors are reserved for applications where the frequencies used are relatively low. Electrolytic capacitors are used where large capacitance is required in a fairly small space, but they are very inefficient at frequencies above 100 kHz or so. In addition, electrolytic capacitors are the first components that we have encountered so far that are polarity sensitive; they only work properly if their positive terminal is at a more positive voltage than the negative terminal. Trimmer capacitors are used when it is necessary to have some adjustment in a circuit for setting up purposes, and are typically found in circuits operating at frequencies of around 50 kHz and upwards. Capacitance is adjusted by turning a screw, which alters either the distance between sets of metal plates separated from each other by insulators, or alters the surface area of the metal plates involved in forming the capacitor, both of which have an effect on the capacitance. Where frequent adjustment of capacity is required, a variable capacitor is used. Here, rotating a shaft moves a set of metal plates relative to another set of fixed plates, and effectively varies the surface area of the plates forming the capacitor. This varies the capacitance. The greater the surface area of the plates forming the capacitor,

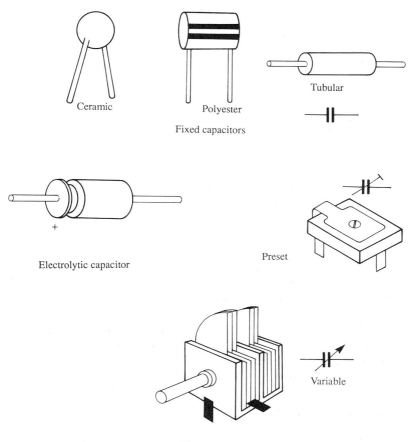

Figure 1.8

the greater the capacitance between them. The most popular use of a variable capacitor is the tuning control of a radio receiver.

Finally, real inductors. Figure 1.9 shows a selection of these components. The air cored coil is often found in circuits handling frequencies of tens or hundreds of megahertz, and the coils wound on some form of cylinder called a *former* are common in radio receiver circuitry. If we put certain materials inside the coil, then the inductance of the coil will be altered; a compound of iron, called a *ferrite*, will increase the inductance whereas brass will decrease the inductance. Increasing the number of turns of wire will also increase the inductance. Coils are very

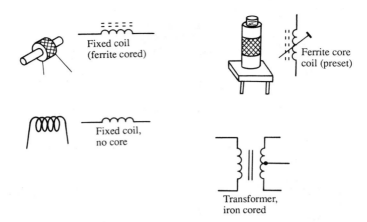

Figure 1.9

rarely truly variable, in that it is awkward to construct the mechanics that would allow the inductance of the coil to be adjusted by a control knob. However, preset inductors are often used, where the position of a ferrite or brass *slug* within the coil of wire can be adjusted, thus varying the inductance. Transformers for use in radio circuits are also often wound using ferrite cores, whereas those for use at lower frequencies, such as mains transformers or those for use with frequencies up to about 20 or 30 kHz can use iron cores.

Component networks

Only by combining the components we have seen so far can we start to get useful circuits. A network is a collection of resistors, capacitors or inductors which takes an input voltage or current and changes the nature of that voltage or current before outputting it. If any one component of the network is changed, then the action of the whole network will be altered. These networks are put to many uses in different branches of electronics, so here we will only deal with the ones that are relevant to us.

Resistor networks

The simplest circuit networks to consider are those featuring only resistors (Figure 1.10). In Figure 1.10a, we have two resistors connected

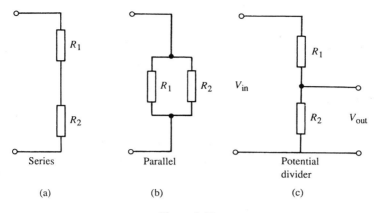

Figure 1.10

end-to-end. Such a connection is called a *series connection*. The resistance offered by this circuit is the sum total of the individual resistors. In mathematical terms, the total resistance is:

$$R_t = R_1 + R_2 + \ldots R_n$$

where R_1, etc. is the resistance of each individual resistor in ohms. Figure 1.10b shows a *parallel* connection of two resistors. Here, the total resistance offered to the flow of current is given by:

$$1/R_t = 1/R_1 + 1/R_2 + \ldots 1/R_n$$

Connecting resistors in series or parallel offers us a method of getting resistances of any particular value we please, as resistors are only manufactured in certain 'off the peg' i.e., *preferred* values.

Figure 1.10c is a special form of resistor network called a *potential divider*. This is used to produce an output voltage which is some fraction of the input voltage.

$$V_{out} = V_{in} \times R_2/(R_1 + R_2)$$

Thus, if we had an input voltage of 9 V, and R1 and R2 were both equal to 1000 ohms, the output voltage would be 4.5 V. The potential divider, in one form or another, is used in circuits to set up a required voltage at a given point in a circuit.

If the output voltage of Figure 1.10c were to be fed into another circuit, then we would have to consider what effect the resistance of that other circuit would have on the potential divider. After all, it would be the same as putting another resistor of that value across R_2, thus making a parallel circuit.

Resistive networks perform in the same way for AC or DC, though at high frequencies resistors may exhibit capacitive or inductive reactance as well as resistance, due to the way the resistor is manufactured. For example, some resistors are made of wire coiled around a ceramic support. These *wire wound resistors* will obviously exhibit some inductance. If such resistors are to be used in circuits where their inductance would contribute significantly to the impedance offered by the resistor to AC, then specially made 'non inductive' wire wound resistors should be used.

The presence of *stray* capacitances or inductances associated with other circuit components can cause serious problems at very high frequencies, where the inductance possessed by even a straight wire, just an inch long can act as a significant impedance to AC flow in the circuit!

Capacitance only

Capacitors connected in series have a total capacitance of:

$$1/C_t = 1/C_1 + 1/C_2 + \ldots 1/C_n$$

which is the same formula as for resistors in parallel. When connected in parallel, capacitors have a total capacitance of:

$$C_t = C_1 + C_2 + \ldots C_n$$

Capacitive dividers can be produced and these are analogous to resistive potential dividers, but act only on AC voltages.

Inductances only

Inductors can be arranged in series and parallel, like resistors or capacitors. For series connected inductors:

$$L_t = L_1 + L_2 + \ldots L_n$$

where L_t stands for the total inductance. For parallel connected inductances, the total inductance is given by:

$$1/L_t = 1/L_1 + 1/L_2 + \ldots 1/L_n$$

This is true when the inductors do not interact with each other in any way, for example, by one inductor being in the magnetic field of another.

Simple RC circuits

RC circuits are circuits containing resistors and capacitors. In radio, these are often to be found performing the task of *filters*, circuits that will allow signals of some frequencies to pass through whilst preventing signals of other frequencies passing.

Figure 1.11a shows a *high pass filter*, which allows AC signals above a certain frequency, called the *cut off frequency* to pass through unaffected whilst reducing the strength of signals below that frequency. Due to the presence of the capacitor, DC signals can not pass through. The higher the value of the resistor and capacitor, the lower the cut off frequency is.

Figure 1.11b shows a *low pass filter*, where only signals below a cut off frequency are passed. Low Pass filters will allow DC through, and the higher R and C are the lower the cut off frequency will be.

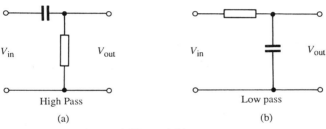

High Pass

(a)

Low pass

(b)

Figure 1.11

Both of these circuits can be examined in greater detail by treating them as resistive potential dividers, using the resistance of the resistor and the capacitive reactance of the capacitor, and substituting these figures in to the potential divider equation that we have already seen. In either case, the cut off frequency occurs when V_{out} equals 0.707 times V_{in}, and is given by:

$$f = 1/(6.28 \times R \times C)$$

More complicated arrangements of resistors and capacitors can create either *bandpass* or *bandstop* filters, in which a particular range of frequencies is either allowed to pass or is attenuated, respectively. Figure 1.12a shows a bandpass filter and the graph of output voltage against frequency. This circuit is called a *Wien bridge*, and turns up quite frequently as part of larger circuits. Figure 1.12b shows a circuit,

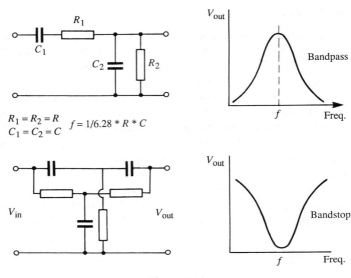

$R_1 = R_2 = R$
$C_1 = C_2 = C$ $f = 1/6.28 * R * C$

Figure 1.12

called a *twin-T filter*, for a bandstop filter and the corresponding graph of output voltage versus frequency. Such graphs are often called *response curves*, or *resonance curves*.

It is not often that resistor–inductor circuits are used, even though a resistor and inductor combination would make quite a good filter. It is just that RC filters are simpler to make and have more predictable behaviour.

Circuits involving capacitance and inductance

When we combine capacitance and inductance in a circuit, we get very interesting effects with AC voltages applied to that circuit. Indeed, without LC circuits radio would not be possible!

A capacitor and an inductor can be combined in series or in parallel (Figure 1.13a and b) and in each case form a special type of circuit called a tuned circuit. At one particular frequency, the resonant frequency, given by:

$$f_r = 1/6.28 \sqrt{LC}$$

the capacitive and inductive reactances will be equal. If we concentrate on the parallel circuit, then the impedance of the circuit when graphed

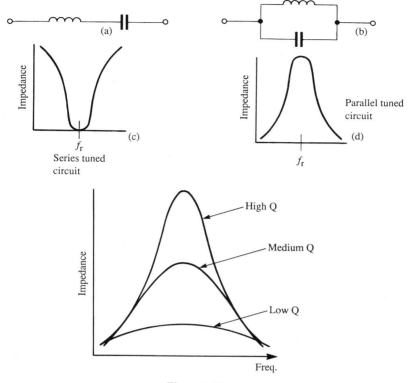

Figure 1.13

against frequency is shown in Figure 1.13d. Thus, signals at this frequency would not pass through the circuit due to its high impedance. This effect is made use of in radio receivers in order to tune particular frequencies in by making one of the components, usually the capacitor, a variable component. Because it rejects the currents caused by signals at the resonant frequency and allows the other signals to pass through unaffected, it is often called a *rejector circuit*.

The resonant frequency for a series circuit is calculated by the same equation, but in this case the impedance of the circuit is very low compared to the impedance at other frequencies, and thus a larger current flows through the circuit at the resonant frequency than at other frequencies. For this reason, such a circuit is often called an *acceptor circuit*.

In a perfect world, tuned circuits like these would exhibit a very sharp increase or decrease in impedance at the resonant frequency. However, losses in the circuit, due primarily to the resistance of the inductor but also the resistance in the wires connecting coil and capacitor, tend to broaden the spread of frequencies over which an impedance change is noticed. The lower the resistance, compared to the reactance of the coil, the sharper will be the impedance change at resonance. The ratio of inductive reactance to resistance is called the *quality factor* (Q) of a tuned circuit, and is often treated as a measure of the 'goodness' of a tuned circuit. The lower the DC resistance of a circuit, the higher the Q and the sharper the resonance curve as shown in Figure 1.13e. Any circuits attached to the tuned circuit will also have effects on the Q of a tuned circuit and, say, connecting a resistance across a tuned circuit will 'flatten out' the resonance curve, and the flatter this curve is the less able is the tuned circuit to differentiate between the desired and undesired signals.

A more detailed view of a resonance curve for a tuned circuit is shown in Figure 1.14, and this introduces the concept of *bandwidth*: the higher the Q of a circuit the narrower the bandwidth of that circuit (bandwidth is commonly measured between two frequencies where, in this example, the impedance is only 70.7% of its resonant frequency

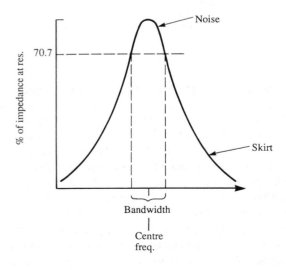

Figure 1.14

value). Clearly, the narrower the bandwidth is the better the differentiation between desired and undesired signals.

When it comes to connecting up these tuned circuits to other circuits, the impedance of any other circuit must be quite close to the impedance of the tuned circuit at resonance for maximum transfer of energy to occur.

LC filters

Just as with resistors and capacitors, inductors and capacitors can be combined together to form low pass or high pass filters (Figure 1.15). The two filters shown are both *pi filters*, so called because the arrangement of inductors and capacitors in the filter is reminiscent of the greek letter π. Such filters can be joined together, the output of one providing the input to the next one, and such *multiple section* filters will work better as filters than single stage ones.

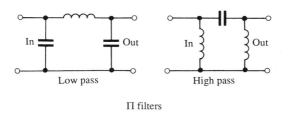

Low pass   High pass

Π filters

Figure 1.15

Active components and circuits

So far, we can do quite a few clever things with voltages and currents, yet there are two vital things we cannot do with the components covered:

1 make signals larger. All the circuits considered so far will actually reduce the signal power, even if only by a small amount

2 actually create AC signals at varying frequencies.

To perform these tasks we need to bring in some new components, called *active devices*, which can, when configured correctly in a circuit, increase the size of signals by a process called *amplification* or produce AC signals by a process called *oscillation*. Active devices require power to do this, and the extra power given to signals in an amplifier circuit comes from the circuit's power supply. In a similar way, we can view an oscillator circuit as a means of converting DC power from, say, a battery into AC signals.

Figure 1.16a shows an idealised view of an amplifier circuit; it has a signal of small size as an input and produces a large copy of this signal at its output. When this reproduction is a faithful copy, the amplifier is said to be *linear*. This is clearly a desirable state of affairs, and great pains are taken to ensure that circuits such as hi-fi amplifiers are as linear as possible. Occasionally, things can go a little wrong, often when we try to get a little bit too much from an amplifier! This is shown in Figure 1.16b, where the output is certainly larger than the input but is no longer a faithful copy. Instead, it has been severely distorted, and a circuit that does this to a signal is said to be *non-linear*.

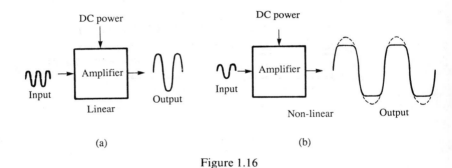

(a)   (b)

Figure 1.16

In the hi-fi amplifier example non-linearity is a disadvantage. Non-linear circuits and components are quite important in some areas of radio and electronics, however, and the simplest non-linear component is a device called a *diode*.

The semiconductor diode

Diodes are made out of special materials, called *semiconductors*, which exhibit interesting electrical properties. I have no intention (or room!) in this book of discussing these materials in detail, but suffice to say the following:

1 semiconductors have a conductivity somewhere between that of

insulators and conductors. They include such materials as silicon and germanium

2 to be of any use, the raw semiconductor material has to have impurities added to it. This process is called *doping*, and depending upon the impurities added, two distinctly different types of semiconducting material are produced – N-type or P-type.

If phosphorus or arsenic atoms, for example, are added to the silicon or germanium base material then the resultant semiconductor has an excess of free electrons. This is N-type semiconducting material, in which the electrons become *charge carriers*, capable of carrying current through it.

The addition of boron, on the other hand, creates a material in which there is an effective deficit of electrons, with the atoms being capable of accepting electrons from other material. This is a P-type semiconductor. The 'vacancies' for these electrons are called *holes* and can be treated, for our purposes, as positive charge carriers.

Useful components are made by combining these two types of semiconductor together. The simplest component is the diode, in which a *PN junction* is created by making one end of a piece of silicon or germanium P and the other end N. Such a junction has a very interesting property; it will only pass an electric current if the P side of the diode is positive with respect to the N side (Figure 1.17a). In this condition, the diode is said to be *forward biased*. If the connections are reversed, no current flows and the diode is said to be *reverse biased* (Figure 1.17b). Diode circuit symbol is shown in Figure 1.17c. The diode is a non-linear component, and its effect on AC signals is shown in Figure 1.17d – only the positive going parts of the signals are passed. This process is called *rectification* or, sometimes, *detection*, the latter specifically being used in radio systems. It is at the heart of radio communications, for it forms the basis of extracting information from a radio wave. You will also hear it referred to sometimes as *demodulation*. Although a perfect diode would conduct when forward biased by even a tiny voltage, real diodes need a certain amount of forward voltage across them before current flow occurs. This is about 0.2 V for diodes based on germanium and 0.6 V for diodes based upon silicon. Until this voltage is reached, no significant current flow occurs.

However, diodes can also perform a variety of other tasks, depending upon how they are manufactured. They can be made so as to produce visible light when forward biased (*light emitting diodes*), to act

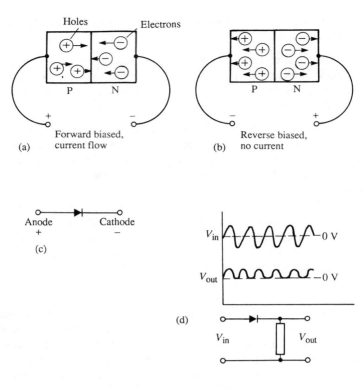

Figure 1.17

as variable capacitors (*varicaps* or *varactors*) or to provide a fixed volt-age output for a varying voltage input (*zener diodes*). Diodes also find widespread use as protection devices in circuits.

Whereas you need to work fairly hard to destroy resistors and capa-citors, diodes and other semiconductors can be damaged in a variety of ways, including:

1 overheating. This might be when soldering the circuit together (Chapter 3), or the part might get too hot in use

2 overloading. Semiconductors need to be operated in such a way as to keep the current through the component and the voltage across the component within the working limits for that component. Exceed-ing either of these parameters can cause irreversible damage.

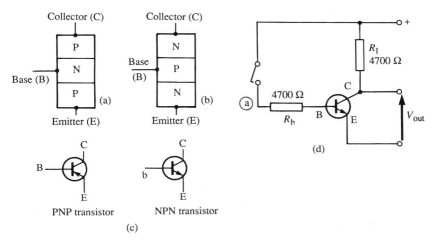

Figure 1.18

Transistors

Although a diode is a useful thing to have around, it still cannot amplify signals or oscillate. To do this we can use a component called a *bipolar transistor*, which is made by joining together three pieces of semiconductor material in the ways shown in Figure 1.18a (a PNP transistor) and b (an NPN transistor). Circuit symbols for both types of transistor are shown in Figure 1.18c. Although transistors may look like two diodes connected back to back, their properties are significantly different. They will only work correctly when the base, emitter and collector connections are connected to appropriate voltage sources. Put briefly, NPN transistors need a base and collector connection that is positive with respect to the emitter connection. PNP transistors need their base and collector connections to be negative with respect to the emitter connection. Figure 1.18d shows a simple circuit which demonstrates the basic nature of a transistor. With the switch open, no current flows into the base of the transistor, the transistor is off, and no current flows from its collector to emitter. In turn, no current flows through the 4700 Ω load resistor, R_l. However, when the switch is closed a small current will flow into the base. The clever bit is that this small current causes a much larger current to flow in the collector-emitter-load part of the circuit; we have effectively amplified the current! In fact, if the load resistance was too low, it would be quite feasible to destroy the transistor because the current passed would be easily sufficient to overheat the transistor junction!

You can probably see that if we apply a varying voltage to point ⓐ, rather than just switching the voltage, we would get a varying current flowing through base resistor R_b and so get a varying current in the load resistor. This would, in turn, cause the voltage at the collector of the transistor to vary, as the transistor and load resistor can be seen as acting as the arms of a potential divider. Thus, a small voltage change at point ⓐ can cause a large voltage change between the transistor collector and 0 V. We have a simple amplifier.

Transistors have 5 major properties that we need to consider when we are using them:

1 V_{ce} – the voltage across the collector and emitter of a transistor. The maximum value of this voltage must not be exceeded

2 I_c – the collector current, flowing through the C and E connections of the transistor. The maximum value must not be exceeded

3 I_b – the base current flowing into the base of a transistor. The maximum value must not be exceeded

4 h_{fe} – a measure of the current 'amplification' or *gain* of the transistor. I_c, the collector current, is equal to $h_{fe}I_b$, the base current, at a given moment in time. This parameter varies between different types of transistor and even within different specimens of the same transistor! Values of h_{fe} can be as low as 10 or 20 or as high as several hundred. The parameter h_{fe} is measured with an input signal of 1000 Hz.

5 f_1 – the frequency at which h_{fe} has fallen to 1. The current gain of a transistor is quite dependant on frequency; generally, the higher in frequency we go the less gain the transistor will provide.

In addition, we should remember that a transistor will also exhibit a tiny amount of capacitance, which will have significant effects at high frequencies and is often the limiting factor in using a particular transistor at a high frequency.

The principal thing to remember is that a bipolar transistor is a *current* amplifier; any voltage that you want to amplify with a transistor circuit must be first converted into a current, and the current flowing through the collector circuit should then be converted back into a voltage by a suitable load. The input current need not be produced by a resistor; if AC signals are being processed the reactance of a capacitor would do the trick, and at high frequencies an inductor could be used as a load. The only other point to note is that transistors, like diodes, will only start working once the voltage between base and emitter is above a certain value. For germanium transistors, this is about 0.2 V and for silicon transistors it is about 0.6 V.

In order for bipolar transistors to work properly, we need to use a resistor network around the transistor to maintain a fixed collector current when no signal input is applied. This is called *biasing* the transistor, and is absolutely essential if we are to have an amplifier that works in a linear fashion. At the heart of biasing (Figure 1.19) is the requirement for the collector voltage (point (a) in Figure 1.19a) to be about half of the supply voltage when there is no input signal. This allows equal voltage swings at point (a), caused by the changing collector current flow when the base current flows in sympathy with the input voltage. Figures 1.19b, c and d show what happens to the output signal in different situations. Figure 1.19b shows the correct output; the voltage swing is such that the peaks of the output sine wave remain smooth curves and are not cut off in any way. Figures 1.19c and d indicate situations in which the output is not a faithful reproduction of the input; distortion has taken place and the amplifier is said to be *non-linear* in action. These non-linearities in circuits can lead to all sorts of problems; for example, a non-linear amplifier could produce output signals at multiples of the input signal frequency. Such *harmonics* are produced by the distorting effect of the amplifier. In addition, you can

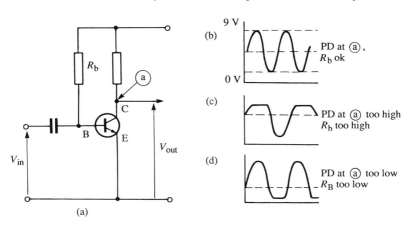

Figure 1.19

probably see that the situation in Figure 1.19d, taken to an extreme, would be similar in action to that of a diode; a non-linear amplifier will thus also act as a detector and will allow us to convert AC signals into a DC signal which is always above 0 V.

Another characteristic possessed by this simple amplifier is that the output signal is 180° out of phase with the input signal. This is called *phase reversal*, and is a common feature of simple amplifier circuits.

The biasing arrangement in Figure 1.19 is very simple, and in real circuits you will see something a little more complicated in use. A more usual biasing arrangement is shown in Figure 1.20. Capacitor *Ce* is selected to give a very low reactance at the frequency the amplifier is working at, and so bypasses the resistor in the emitter lead of the transistor at AC but has no effect at DC. The biasing arrangement of Figure 1.20 protects the transistor against a very nasty occurrence called *thermal runaway*; in simple biasing arrangements, should the transistor start heating up, the collector current increases, which leads to a further heating effect, and so on, eventually destroying the transistor. The arrangement of resistors in Figure 1.20 prevents this from occuring.

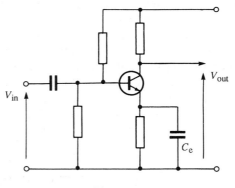

Figure 1.20

Transistor amplifiers come in three basic designs, called the *common emitter, common collector*, and *common base* designs. These designations depend upon how the inputs and outputs from the circuits are arranged, and Figure 1.21 shows the three different designs. You may ask why we have three separate types of circuit; well, it all depends on (1) what sort of gain we want from a circuit, (2) what sort of impedance circuits we are getting the input signal from and (3) what impedance we

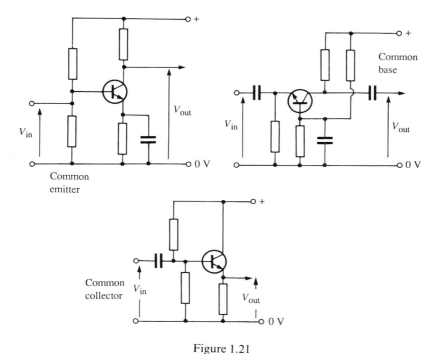

Figure 1.21

are driving as an output. You may remember that for maximum transfer of signal to occur between two circuits, impedances need to be similar, and so it is quite important that the amplifier configuration we choose for a particular job has the correct input and output impedances as well as being able to supply some gain.

Common emitter
This is probably the most popular amplifier configuration. It has an input impedance of between 600 and 2000 Ω, and an output impedance of anywhere between a few ohms and 25 kΩ. The exact values depend upon the values of resistors in the circuit. This circuit exhibits phase reversal.

Common collector
It has a very high input impedance and a quite low output impedance. This makes it useful for matching high impedance circuits to low impedance circuits. Again, exact values depend upon the values of the resis-

tors in the circuit. The output signal of the common collector amplifier is in phase with the input.

Common base
Here we have a very low input impedance and a high output impedance. This circuit is often used with signal sources that have a very low impedance, such as radio receiving aerials (Chapter 9). Again, the output is in phase with the input.

As we might expect from amplifying circuits, these three configurations will all increase the *power* of the signal, but they do so in different ways. If we remember that power is equal to current multiplied by voltage, then:

Common emitter   – current and voltage gain both high.
Common base   – current gain less than 1, voltage gain high.
Common collector – current gain high, voltage gain 1.

Field effect transistors

Before further investigating some simple circuits, we should examine another type of transistor that is common in radio work – the *field effect transistor* (FET). It comes in two basic operational types, the *P-channel FET* and the *N-channel FET*, and circuit symbols are shown in Figure 1.22 along with a simple N-channel FET amplifier. The FET

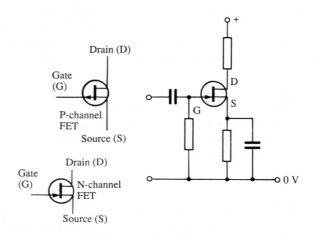

Figure 1.22

is often referred to as a semiconductor valve, as it has a few things in common with the valves that preceeded transistors in radio receivers. Whereas the transistor we have discussed so far (the bipolar transistor) is effectively a current controlled device (where a small current flowing into the base causes a large current to flow in the emitter–collector circuit), the FET is a voltage controlled device, where a small change in voltage at the input can cause a large voltage swing at the output. In addition, the FET has a very large input impedance which allows it to take signals friom other circuits without affecting their operation by loading them. For example, a FET amplifier could be used to amplify the output of a parallel tuned circuit (by connecting the tuned circuit between gate and source) without seriously affecting the value of the Q of that circuit, because the high input impedance of the FET would not damp the tuned circuit. On the other hand, if you connect a parallel tuned circuit directly between the base and emitter of a common emitter amplifier you would seriously dampen the circuit, causing it to become less selective.

The FETs we have seen here are examples of *junction FETs*, sometimes called JFETs, or JUGFETs. Another form of FET is the *insulated gate FET* (IGFET) of which the MOSFET (metal oxide semiconductor FET) is the most famous example.

Multi-stage circuits

Although each of these amplifier circuits will work by itself, it is usual to connect them up into more complicated circuits. In such complex circuits, we often split the circuit up into *stages* when we are attempting to see how it works. Signals are taken from the output of one stage into the input of the next stage – this is called *inter-stage coupling*, and there are a variety of ways to go about it:

1 *direct coupling*. A connection is taken from the output of one stage to the input of the next stage. This is not often seen in radio equipment, as such a connection would allow both the AC signal and DC voltages to pass between the two stages. This may upset the biasing of the stages, and so is not usually done.

2 *capacitive coupling*. Here, coupling between the two stages is via a capacitor, which will allow AC signals to pass but will block the DC biasing voltages. A simple capacitor-coupled two stage amplifier is shown in Figure 1.23. This will often have an effect on the way in

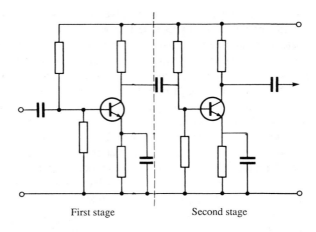

First stage   Second stage

Figure 1.23

which different frequencies are amplified by the circuit, as the react-ance of the capacitor, and hence the amount of signal passed through, varies with frequency.

3. *transformer coupling*. Some circuits use transformers to couple circuits.

Broadband and tuned amplifiers

We often want amplifiers to work over as wide a range of frequencies as possible. An amplifier with this characteristic is called a *broadband* amplifier, and some of these circuits will give as good amplification at 1 MHz as they do at 1 kHz. These amplifiers are said to have a wide bandwidth. Unfortunately, the wider a circuit's bandwidth, the more noise will be produced and amplified by that circuit and will be heard by us, for example, in the headphones or loudspeaker of our receivers. Noise, in electronic terms, is caused by the random motion of electrons in circuit components, and we often want to reduce the amount of noise in a circuit without reducing the level of the signal being pro-cessed by the circuit. The ratio of signal strength to noise level is called the *signal-to-noise ratio* (S/N ratio), and we can easily improve the situation by limiting the bandwidth of the amplifier to that required to reproduce the desired signal without losing any part of it. For example,

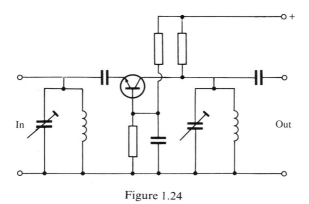

Figure 1.24

for a hi-fi system we would want to consider an amplifier with the ability to reproduce frequencies from a few hertz to around 20 kHz. We can do this by simply building low pass filters in to the amplifier, in this case with a cut off point of, say, 20 kHz. We can take this argument even further, and build an amplifier which will only give good gain over a relatively small frequency range. Such a circuit is called a *tuned amplifier*, and a simple one is shown in Figure 1.24. The parallel tuned circuit at the input is chosen to be resonant at the frequency of interest, and so the amplifier will show maximum output signal at that frequency. Tuned amplifiers are of crucial importance in radio circuits, and often you will find several stages tuned to the same frequency to give a very selective tuned amplifier with considerable gain.

Feedback and oscillators

Why anyone ever thought of connecting a circuit so that some of the output signal could be passed back to the input is quite a mystery to me, but without this technique we would not be able to produce the radio signals that we are interested in receiving. This technique is called *feedback*, and there are two distinct types.

Negative feedback

Here, the output signal is out of phase with the input signal, and so the two signals tend to cancel each other out somewhat. This has the effect of reducing the amplification of a given stage, but has some beneficial effect, including a reduction in circuit noise, greater bandwidth,

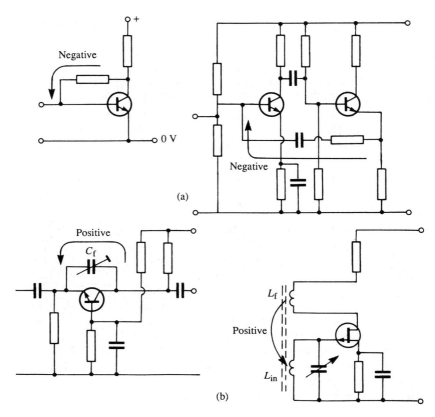

Figure 1.25

reduced distortion and greater reproducibility. The latter is particularly important in commercial designs, where production line assembly of circuits is used: greater feedback makes the performance of a circuit less dependant upon the parameters of transistors. When negative feedback is used in circuits, more amplifier stages are required to get the same amount of gain as was obtained using circuits which did *not* incorporate negative feedback. Figure 1.25a shows methods of applying negative feedback to circuits.

Positive feedback

If the output signal is in phase with the input signal, then positive feedback occurs. This increases the gain of the circuit, often to a point where oscillation begins and the circuit begins to produce signals all by itself! When this occurs in circuits where oscillation is not required, it is called *instability*, and care has to be taken to stop it. Positive feedback reduces the bandwidth of a circuit and so makes it more selective. Figure 1.25b shows methods of introducing positive feedback in a circuit. In the common base circuit, there is no need to worry about the phase of the output and input signals, as they are always in phase with each other in this configuration. The feedback is controlled by the size of C_f. However, with a common emitter circuit, the output is 180° out of phase with the input and so we have to do something to reverse the phase of the output to make it in phase with the input. A quick way of doing this is with a transformer, and in this instance the feedback would be controlled by the coupling between L_f and L_{in}.

Positive feedback, when controlled, can be used to vastly increase the gain of a circuit, and this is put to good use in certain types of simple radio receiver (Chapter 5). However, positive feedback can also be used to make a circuit which produces signals rather than just amplifies them. Such a circuit is called an oscillator, and consists of an amplifier with a positive feedback path and a means of selecting the frequencies that are fed back, so that positive feedback is strongest at one frequency alone. This causes the oscillator to produce signals at that one frequency. A simple oscillator is shown in Figure 1.26, where the fre-

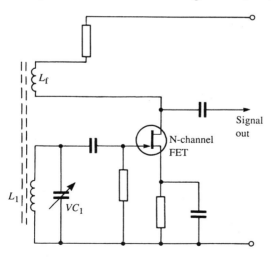

Figure 1.26

quency of oscillation is controlled by VC_1 and L_1. Feedback comes from L_f. On turning on the circuit, small voltages would appear at the gate of the FET due to noise in the circuit. This will be amplified, and fed back via L_f, thus causing a self-sustaining oscillation at the frequency determined by L_1 and VC_1.

The need for linearity is important in oscillators as well as amplifiers, and distortion of the signals produced here can give an output that consists of more than one frequency due to the generation of harmonic signals. So, oscillators are biased in a similar way to amplifiers.

Although the frequency determining section of this oscillator was based on an LC circuit, you can have oscillators at lower frequencies whose frequency is controlled by resistors and capacitors. There is also no need for the signal produced by an oscillator to be a sinewave, although in radio this is the most common signal type produced. Square waves or triangular waves can be produced by suitable circuits. For oscillators where it is required to generate a specific frequency, such as exactly 1 MHz, a circuit element called a *crystal* is used. Without going into the technicalities, this acts as a fixed frequency tuned circuit with a Q that is much larger than we could get from a tuned circuit based upon coils and capacitor, and is almost always used where a fixed frequency signal of high accuracy is required.

Integrated circuits

Advances in technology have allowed the production of a complete circuit on a single small chip of silicon and these devices, now quite cheap and easy to use, are called *integrated circuits* (ICs). Their advantages are obvious; they make equipment simpler to design, build and test. When using them in circuits, we generally need to provide a few resistors, capacitors and inductors to make them work, but the majority of the 'gubbins' is tucked up inside the packaging of the IC. There are two main families of integrated circuit:

1 **Linear ICs.** These are integrated circuits carrying such devices as amplifiers or oscillators, and are used to process AC signals in some way. Elsewhere in this book, you will find reference to an LM380 audio amplifier IC. This is a typical linear integrated circuit. Other devices available include whole radio receivers on a chip, high-gain amplifiers and oscillators capable of producing sine, square and triangle waves

2 **Digital ICs.** These chips are used in computers and similar circuits which perform logical counting tasks. They take inputs which are in the form of pulses which represent binary 1s or 0s, rather than AC signals, and are not used directly in radio receiving equipment. However, we will use a couple of these logic chips in Chapter 10, and they are also used in equipment used to measure the frequency of AC signals.

The only disadvantage of IC packages is what you might call the 'all your eggs in one basket' syndrome! If you damage a transistor, you plug another one in, and transistors are not all that expensive. If you damage a transistor within an IC package, then you cannot just replace that one component; you must replace the whole package.

Electromechanical components

As well as all these wonderful semiconductors, resistors, capacitors and inductors, we should not forget the more mundane bits and pieces without which none of these components would be much use. For example, what good would an amplifier be if we had no means of converting the electrical signals into sound waves in the air?

Loudspeakers and earphones

In its simplest form, a loudspeaker consists of a fixed magnet, around which is wound a coil of wire connected to a paper cone. When current flows through the wire, a magnetic field is produced which interacts with that produced by the fixed magnet. This causes the paper coil to move in sympathy with the current, thus moving the paper cone to which it is attached. This produces sound signals in the air. The coil of wire is quoted as having an impedance, often in the region of 4 to 80 Ω. Many circuits today use 8 Ω loudspeakers. Loudspeakers come in a variety of sizes, and generally the bigger the speaker the louder and richer the sound produced. Small speakers tend to produce a rather 'tinny' sound, as they are just not up to reproducing the lower frequency sounds accurately, although they can reproduce the higher pitched sounds.

It is occasionally more convenient to listen to a signal with headphones or an earphone. Most of these work on the same principle as the loudspeaker, and have similar impedances. Some earpieces, called *crystal earpieces* have a very high impedance, and these use an effect called the *piezoelectric* effect. A thin crystal is mounted between two metal plates and whenever a voltage is applied to the plates the crystal moves in sympathy. This crystal is connected to a diaphragm – the equivalent of the paper cone in the loudspeaker – and sound is produced. However, the quality of the sound produced leaves a lot to be desired and where possible you are better off using one of the other types of earphone.

Switches

Simple things, but quite useful! A switch is simply a mechanical means of joining or separating two conductors, thus starting or stopping the flow of current. Some allow current to be passed down different paths in a circuit, depending upon the switch setting.

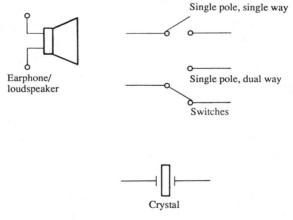

Figure 1.27

Circuit symbols for these electromechanical components are shown in Figure 1.27.

I hope that this chapter has given you some insight into the world of electronics. There is a lot we have not looked at, and I suggest having a look at some of the books listed in Appendix 3 if you want more in-depth information.

TWO

Radio waves

A radio wave is an example of something called electromagnetic radiation, like X-rays, visible light or the microwaves produced by a microwave oven.

Radio waves consist of two parts – a varying magnetic field and a varying electrical field, which are at 90° to each other, and to the direction in which the radio wave is travelling (Figure 2.1a). Any electrical conductor carrying a changing electrical current will generate a radio wave around it, and this wave spreads out into space, as shown in Figure 2.1b. Similarly, a radio wave encountering a conductor will induce tiny voltages across that conductor. This is the principle behind the simplest of all radio aerials – a wire suspended in the air.

How we describe radio waves

We use a variety of terms to describe the radio wave. It has a speed, or *velocity*, of around 300 000 000 metres per second in free space. This speed varies slightly if the wave travels through materials having different electrical properties to air, but for our purposes can be considered constant. As you can see from Figure 2.1a, the distance between two similar parts of the wave is called the *wavelength* λ measured in metres. The distance between a signal peak and the zero line is called the *amplitude* of the wave. If the speed of the radio wave is constant, then the wavelength depends upon the number of *cycles* (a cycle is a single, complete wave – i.e. it is one wavelength long) generated in a given length of time. The number of cycles occurring in a second is the *frequency* of the wave, and is measured in hertz, like the frequency of the AC signals we saw in Chapter 1. You will soon find yourself using kilohertz (kHz) i.e. thousands of hertz, and megahertz

39

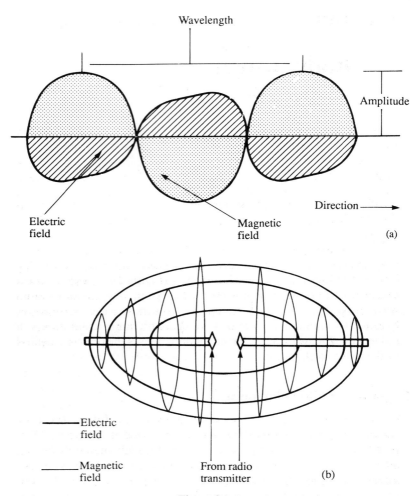

Figure 2.1

(MHz) i.e. millions of hertz, to describe the frequencies of radio waves. The frequency of a radio wave is, if you like, its 'fingerprint'.

We can convert between frequency and wavelength for radio waves using the following equations. In each case, wavelength is in metres and frequency is in hertz:

frequency   = 300 000 000/wavelength
wavelength = 300 000 000/frequency

For example, let's convert a wavelength of 200 metres into a frequency:

$$\text{frequency} = 300\,000\,000/200$$
$$= 3\,000\,000/2$$
$$= 1\,500\,000\,\text{Hz}$$
$$= 1500\,\text{kHz}$$
$$= 1.5\,\text{MHz}$$

In the past, the frequencies on which radio stations were operating were quoted in terms of wavelength, but today most stations give their frequency in kilohertz or megahertz. One anachronism; you will still hear talk of the 20 metre band, or the 19 metre band whilst listening to the radio. These are not single frequencies, though, but ranges of frequencies.

Propagation of a radio wave

A radio wave, once in space, travels in a straight line unless something happens to change its direction. In order to change a radio wave's direction, it must be either *reflected* or *refracted*. Reflection of radio waves is the basis of *radar*; the waves are bounced off an object and are reflected back to where they came from. Refraction, the 'bending' of radio waves, is the means by which radio signals can get from one side of the globe to the other.

The study of the way in which radio waves travel is called the study of radio wave *propagation*. A radio wave is said to be propagated from one point to another. We are still learning a lot about the way radio waves travel, but early work in the field showed that radio waves could travel a long distance round the world – much further than would be possible if the wave were going in a straight line. It was found that an area of the Earth's upper atmosphere called the *ionosphere* was responsible for refracting radio waves back to earth many hundreds or even thousands of miles away from their origin, thus giving us a means of communicating around the world. We will look at propagation in greater detail in Chapter 13.

Categories of radio waves

Radio waves are categorised for official purposes into the following groups of frequencies:

    ELF   extra low frequency 0–3 kHz

VLF   very low frequency 3–30 kHz
LF   low frequency 30–300 kHz
MF   medium frequency 300–3000 kHz
HF   high frequency 3000–30 000 kHz
VHF   very high frequency 30 MHz–300 MHz
UHF   ultra high frequency 300 MHz–3000 MHz

There are frequencies higher than these, but we are not really concerned with them. In fact, this book only covers those frequencies up to 30 MHz. We tend to call the frequencies between 1.6 MHz and 30 MHz *short wave* frequencies.

Heterodynes

It is possible to combine two radio waves by a process called *mixing*. This can either happen in the ionosphere, as we will see later in the book, or in an electronic circuit that is not acting in a truly linear manner after the radio waves have been converted into electrical signals by a receiving aerial. However it happens, the result of the mixing process will be signals of new frequencies in addition to the frequencies that were mixed (Figure 2.2). A resultant frequency is called a *beat frequency* or *heterodyne*. We often hear this signal as a whistle in the loudspeaker of the radio when tuning across radio stations that are close together in frequency. A heterodyne's frequency is given by the

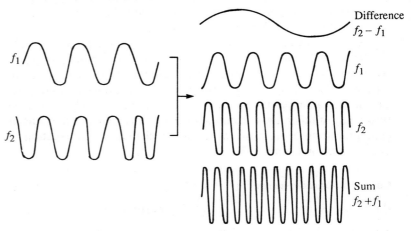

Figure 2.2

mathematical subtraction or addition of the original two frequencies, so that:

$$f_s = f_1 + f_2$$

or:

$$f_d = f_1 - f_2$$

f_1 and f_2 are the frequencies of the original signals. The heterodyne caused by subtracting the two original frequencies (f_d) is called the *difference* signal, while the heterodyne created by the addition (f_s) is called the *sum* signal.

The sum and difference signals are called the *mixing products* of the two original radio signals. There are other mixing products caused if the f_s and f_d signals combine with f_1 or f_2, but we need not be too concerned about these. As an example, we can work out the sum and difference signals obtained by mixing a 10 000 kHz signal and a 10 005 kHz signal:

$$f_d = 10\,005 - 10\,000$$
$$f_d = 5 \;\; kHz$$

and:

$$f_s = 10\,005 + 10\,000$$
$$f_s = 20\,005\,kHz$$

The sum and difference signals, f_s and f_d, are most useful in radio receivers and in allowing us to 'read' certain types of radio signal, as we will later find out.

Modulation

To be of any use to us, a radio wave needs to carry information in some way. The process of putting information on to a radio wave is called *modulation*. A radio wave carrying information is said to be modulated. There are a variety of ways in which we can modulate a radio wave, and they all rely on varying some parameter of the radio wave, such as its amplitude or frequency.

A radio wave being transmitted without any information on it in theory occupies just a single frequency (Figure 2.3a). The frequency of an unmodulated signal is called the *carrier* frequency, and the signal is called the *carrier wave*, because it will carry the information. In actual fact, the frequency 'space' taken up by a typical radio wave is more like that shown in Figure 2.3b. This shows the *bandwidth* of a modulated

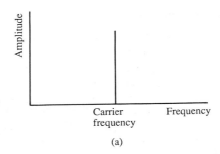

(a)

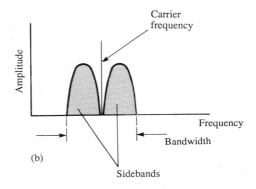

Figure 2.3

radio signal – the amount of space that a signal takes up in the frequency spectrum. As we put more information on to a carrier wave, the bandwidth taken up by the radio wave increases. Put simply, the more information carried by the carrier wave in a certain length of time, the wider the bandwidth of the signal.

The frequencies either side of the carrier are called *sidebands*. There are two of these; the *lower sideband* (LSB) is below the carrier in frequency and the *upper sideband* (USB) is above the carrier. All methods of modulation generate these sidebands, though their relative size depends upon the method of modulation used. In general terms, though, half the power of the radio signal resides in the carrier wave, the remaining power being shared between the two sidebands. One point to remember is that when we quote the frequency of a radio signal, we are actually quoting the frequency of the carrier wave, not the frequencies used by the sidebands.

Channels

Because modulated signals 'spread out' away from the carrier frequency, it should be clear that if we have two stations close together, both with fairly wide sidebands, we are going to cause interference. For this reason, frequencies used for broadcasting are split into *channels* on which stations can broadcast. The channels are separated in frequency so that the interference between stations on adjacent channels is small. In the long and medium wave broadcast bands, for example, the channel spacing depends on the part of the world: in Europe it is 9 kHz, whilst in the US it is 10 kHz. Thus, in Europe when you tune across the medium wave broadcast band you will find stations every 9 kHz. In the short wave broadcast bands spacing is 5 kHz all over the world. Stations can occasionally be heard between these channels, though they are likely to suffer heavy interference from the stations on the channels either side of them.

On frequencies used for such things as ship-to-shore radio, channel spacing is different to this, and some frequencies, such as those used by radio amateurs, do not have channelling at all. Where channelling is used, it helps reduce interference and heterodynes between stations. Channel separation is always a compromise. If we were to increase it, interference would be less but to fit the same number of channels in we would increase the total bandwidth used by all the channels. If we decrease the spacing to decrease the total bandwidth used by a given number of channels, then we would increase interference between channels.

Types of modulation

Over the years, a variety of techniques have evolved to put information on to radio waves. Each method of modulation has been given a 3 character designation by the International Telecommunications Union (ITU) so that people in different parts of the world can refer to particular modulation methods by the same name. Let us look at those you are likely to encounter on the air in the short wave range.

Continuous wave

Known also as CW, information is transmitted by simply turning the radio transmitter on and off. Messages are often sent in *morse code* (see Chapter 12), in which letters, numbers and other characters are sent as a series of long and short pulses from the radio transmitter. Figure 2.4

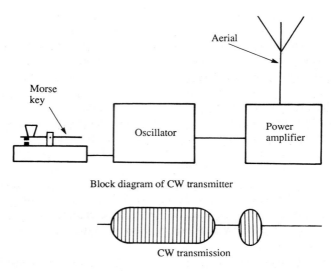

Block diagram of CW transmitter

CW transmission

Figure 2.4

shows a block diagram of a simple morse transmitter. It is this simplicity that has made CW a popular means of communication for radio amateurs, who can build a simple CW transmitter and receiver for a few pounds. CW is also widely used for signalling at sea.

The principal advantage of CW is its penetrating power and its narrow bandwidth. A morse signal can be read and understood in conditions where a voice signal might not even be audible! A typical bandwidth for a CW transmission would be just a few hundred hertz, so quite a few CW transmissions can be fitted into, say 5 kHz of frequency space. The disadvantages are that the amount of information that can be transmitted in a given time is fairly small, depending upon the speed at which the morse is transmitted. In addition, to make head or tail of CW transmissions you need to know morse! The ITU designation for CW transmissions is A1A.

Amplitude modulation
This is abbreviated to AM, and its ITU designation is A3E. The information to be carried on the radio wave is carried as variations in the amplitude of the carrier waves. AM is the most widely used form of modulation for short wave broadcasting, and virtually all stations in the various short wave broadcast bands use it for transmitting speech

and music. Any mode that allows speech or other sound signals to be transmitted is called a *telephony* mode. Figure 2.5a shows a block diagram of an AM transmitter, while Figure 2.5b shows how the carrier wave appears after modulation.

The big advantages of AM are that it is fairly easy to produce, it can transmit voice and music – a big plus over CW – and it can be received on very simple radio receivers.

The main disadvantage lies in the bandwith taken up by such signals. The bandwidth of an AM signal is given by:

$$\text{bandwidth} = 2 \times f_\text{h}$$

where f_h is the frequency of the highest frequency signal from the audio amplifier stage of the AM transmitter that is to be used to modulate the radio wave. Thus if we had an audio signal of 5 kHz that was to modulate the carrier wave, the bandwidth of this signal would be 10 kHz. If this were the only audio tone to modulate the carrier, then the sidebands would be as shown in Figure 2.5c. However, speech and music are made up of many different frequencies, so we end up with the situation in Figure 2.5d. We can limit the bandwidth of an AM signal by keeping the highest frequency reaching the modulator as low as possible without losing too much quality from the received signal.

Single sideband

Single sideband, or SSB, is a popular modulation method for amateurs, aviation, shipping and various other utility stations that use the radio spectrum. Its ITU designation is J3E, and it is another telephony mode.

The bandwidth of an SSB transmission is about half that of an AM transmission carrying the same information. This reduction in bandwidth is possible because the two sidebands of an AM transmission both carry the same information. One sideband could thus be disposed of without losing any of the transmitted information. This is precisely what SSB does. In fact, it goes one step further than this; most SSB transmitters also remove the carrier wave, thus concentrating all the available transmitter power in to the remaining sideband. This, along with the fact that SSB signals are less prone to fading and interference due to the reduced bandwidth, gives SSB signals the ability to be understood where AM signals might not be. The reduced bandwidth relative to AM has resulted in plans to replace all AM broadcast transmitters in the short wave bands with SSB transmitters by the year 2015.

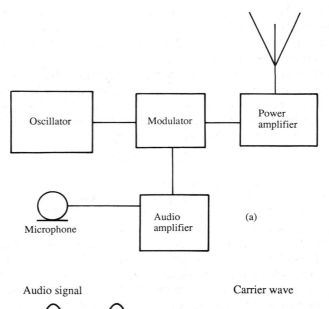

Oscillator — Modulator — Power amplifier

Microphone — Audio amplifier

(a)

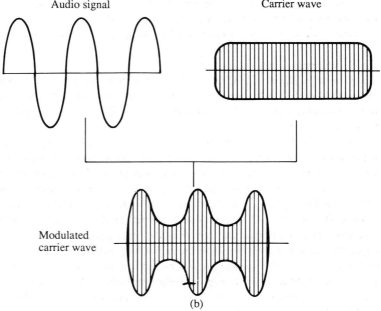

Audio signal

Carrier wave

Modulated carrier wave

(b)

Figure 2.5

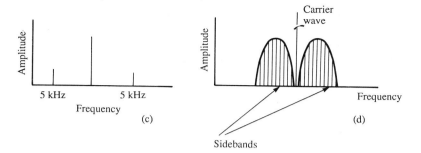

Figure 2.5 (cont.)

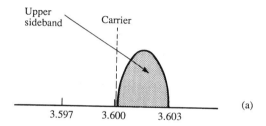

(a)

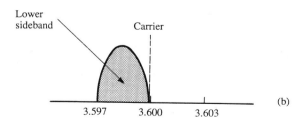

(b)

Figure 2.6

Figure 2.6 shows the two different types of SSB signal that you are likely to encounter. *Lower sideband*, or LSB (Figure 2.6a) is produced by removing the upper sideband and the carrier. *Upper sideband*, or USB (Figure 2.6b) is produced by removing the lower sideband and carrier. The dotted line shows the position of where the carrier would have been in each case.

The disadvantage of SSB is that it requires some special receiving techniques to recover the signals. When we receive an SSB signal, we need to provide a signal to replace the carrier wave, in the correct position with respect to the sideband, before the voice will become intelligible. We will look at this in greater detail in later chapters. There are some forms of SSB transmission where the carrier is left alone; in these cases the signal can often be understood without special receivers. In addition, SSB transmitters are a little more involved as they require special filters to remove the unwanted sideband and carrier wave, or circuits to generate the single sideband without a carrier.

Narrow band frequency modulation
This mode, abbreviated to NBFM and given the ITU designation F3E, is not widely used below about 30 MHz. However, its main use in the UK is on Citizens' Band radio, with frequencies around 27 MHz, and by radio amateurs, often around 29.5 MHz.

It is another telephony mode, though this time the radio wave is modulated by varying its frequency rather than its amplitude. Figure 2.7 shows an NBFM signal. In theory, an NBFM signal can be shown to have sidebands of infinite width; however, practice shows us that an NBFM signal has about the same bandwidth as an AM signal provided that the modulating frequencies are the same in each case. NBFM signals can be detected by an AM receiver, or a special circuit can be used for better quality.

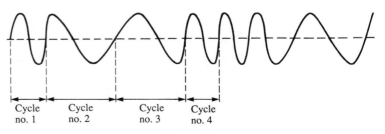

Figure 2.7

Radio teletype

This is different to the other modes we have seen in that it can not be understood by just listening to it. Radio teletype is abbreviated to RTTY and is a method of transmitting typed text rapidly using a radio signal. Letters typed are transmitted either by varying the frequency of the radio wave (FSK – frequency shift keying) or by transmitting a series of audio tones (AFSK – audio frequency shift keying). The code used is called *baudot* code, and at the receiving end the tones are used to control a machine to print out the transmitted message. Alternatively, a computer can be programmed to convert the received tones into text for display on a computer monitor screen. We will look at RTTY decoding in greater detail in Chapter 15.

The advantage of RTTY is that a great deal of text can be transmitted quickly by anyone who can type. The disadvantage is that special equipment is required to read the signals and that the signals are prone to interference. RTTY is widely used by amateurs, news agencies and other stations, such as weather stations. On the maritime frequencies, however, RTTY is being gradually replaced by other methods of text transmission.

Each of these modulation methods requires us to use our radio receiver in different ways to get the best reception possible. We will cover this topic in Chapter 11, when I will examine how to get the best from your radio set.

THREE

Practical matters

Now we know a little electronics, and have an idea of what a radio wave is, we can get down to building receivers.

The tools and techniques used are not too involved, and need not be expensive. A good minimum collection of tools is:

Soldering equipment

Good joints in any electronic circuit require soldering – this is the process of joining up two pieces of metal by melting a metal alloy with a very low melting point (the solder) around the joint and letting it solidify. You will need a 15 watt electrical soldering iron with a variety of bits. Do not be tempted to use the soldering equipment used by plumbers or engineers; you are most likely to end up melting your radio! As an alternative to an iron, a soldering gun may be used, having the advantage that it does not have to 'warm up' like a soldering iron. Soldering equipment often comes complete with a few accessories, such as heat sinks to help protect sensitive components from the effects of heat. A soldering iron stand is a good buy as well, reducing risk of scorched table tops or fingers!

You will also need solder; use flux-cored electronics grade solder which comes in reels. A 500 gram reel will last a *very* long time! The flux contained in the solder is a chemical that allows the solder to flow freely around the joint that is being made. Do not be tempted to use separate flux and bar solder as used by plumbers. I use 22 SWG reeled solder, which is adequate for all the work we will be doing.

Screwdrivers

A useful purchase is a set of good jewellers screwdrivers, as well as a couple of larger ones for heavier jobs.

Wire strippers and pliers

Your dentist will tell you not to use your front teeth for stripping the insulation from wire. Instead, a pair of wire strippers can be purchased. Get a pair which allows you to set, usually by means of a small wheel, the diameter of the wire being stripped. This will help prevent you damaging the copper wire when you strip off the insulation.

A pair of long nosed radio pliers is also useful, as are a pair of side cutters for cutting wire to length. Wire strippers can be used to cut wire, but the side cutters tend to be more convenient for thicker wires or cables.

Hole drilling equipment

You will need to drill out a few holes for mounting controls on front panels, etc. You can manage with a manual drill, but an electric drill is very useful. Get bits from $\frac{1}{16}$ in to $\frac{3}{8}$ in (or 1 mm to 10 mm, if you prefer), if possible, and ensure they are capable of drilling light steel. A drill stand is a useful extra, but not really essential. A very useful tool is a reamer, used for widening holes to the exact size required. A round file is also handy for this sort of job, though if you are working aluminium you will find it tends to clog up files with dust.

Miscellaneous

A small vice, screwed down to a piece of wood is very useful for giving you a 'third hand'. I find an old toothbrush and a pair of tweezers to be quite useful, along with a craft knife. In addition, a spot face cutter will be required if you use Veroboard for building your circuits on, and a small hacksaw will be needed for cutting the shafts of potentiometers, etc. to size.

Though not in the 'tools' category, a small testmeter is a worthwhile buy. Look for one that is quoted as being *20 000 ohms per volt* or thereabouts, covering volts up to at least 500, current up to around an amp and resistance. This will be a useful aid when building sets, and should not be too expensive.

These tools can be bought from a variety of sources; a good ironmongers or tool shop in the high street will be able to supply them, as will some of the component stockists listed in Appendix 1.

Components

The circuits in this book use parts that are fairly easily available. Stockists listed in Appendix 1 provided the author with the components used in the prototype circuits.

Alternatively, parts may be salvaged from old receivers. This is a particularly useful source for loudspeakers, tuning capacitors, potentiometers, etc. but in modern receivers attempts to recover the semiconductors or even capacitors and resistors can fail due to the small size of the circuit boards involved – it is possible to destroy components whilst desoldering them! Wire of specified standard wire gauges, for coil winding, can be purchased in 2 oz spools or can be recovered from old equipment. If you salvage your wire then check the insulation; the enamel covering on any wire should be in good condition, and not scratched or discoloured.

Where possible, adhere to the component values given, particularly in tuned circuits or RF amplifiers, where even a small deviation could cause problems. However, the circuits described will all work with 5% tolerance resistors and 'off the shelf' capacitors.

Component markings

Resistor values are not usually printed on the component body. Instead, a system of coloured bands is used to indicate the value of the component. The resistor colour code is shown in Figure 3.1. The exact meaning for given colour depends upon the position of the band on the component. As an example, consider the following:

First band	yellow	4
Second band	violet	7
Third band	red	× 100
Fourth band	silver	10% tolerance

Thus we have a 4700 ohm resistor, with a tolerance of 10%. A similar code is used on some types of capacitor (Figure 3.2). On other types of capacitor, the value is printed on the component. For example, you may read 0.01 on a capacitor – this is 0.01 μF. Alternatively, the value might be written as 681 – in this instance, the third digit indicates the number of zeroes and the capacitor value will be in pF. So, our 681 capacitor actually has a value of 680 pF. Lack of a third digit indicates no zeroes; thus 47 would be 47 pF, and 102 would be 1000 pF. On some capacitors, you will see the value indicated directly: so 22 n indicates a

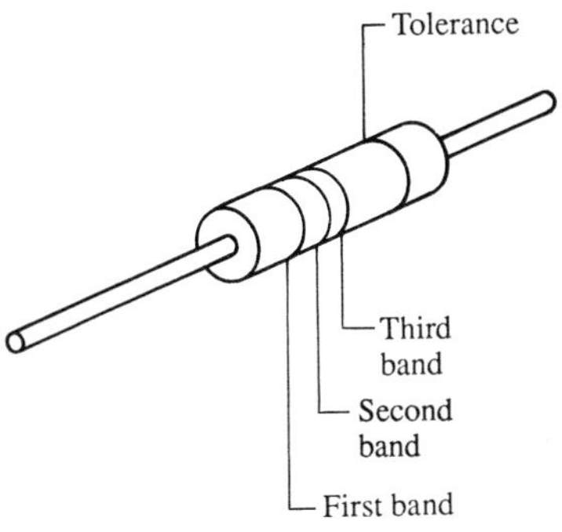

Colour	Value (Bands 1 + 2)	Power of ten (Band 3)	Tolerance
Black	0	1	–
Brown	1	10	–
Red	2	100	–
Orange	3	1000	–
Yellow	4	10000	–
Green	5	100 000	–
Blue	6	1000 000	–
Violet	7	10 000 000	–
Grey	8	100 000 000	–
White	9	1000 000 000	–
Gold	0.1	–	±5%
Silver	0.01	–	±10%
No colour	–	–	±20%

Figure 3.1

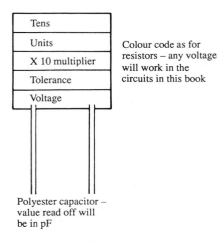

Figure 3.2

22 nF capacitor. Electrolytic capacitors have their values on them in μF.

The circuits in this book all use $\frac{1}{4}$ watt resistors. The only other thing to consider is the working voltage of electrolytic capacitors – components of 16 V or above working voltage should be used. Semiconductor pin-outs will be discussed when we come to use them in circuits. In the main interference filters, special high voltage capacitors must be used.

Construction techniques

There are several ways to build the circuits in this book, and here I will give a quick description of some of them.

Solderless techniques

There are three methods of building circuits that do not need soldering. The first of these uses *solderless breadboards* (Figure 3.3) where component leads are pushed into holes which are connected into groups by conductors inside the plastic body of the breadboard. They are quite handy for some circuits, and you can get 'front panels' for them on which to mount controls. However, for radio circuits they have two main drawbacks:

1 the boards are not too good for connections involving very fine wires

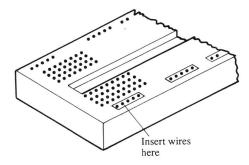

Figure 3.3

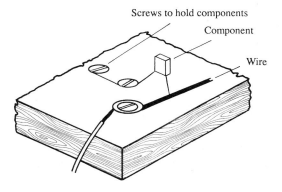

Figure 3.4

2 there is a capacitance, as much as 5 pF, between adjacent strips on the breadboard. This can cause problems with unwanted coupling (see later) between different parts of the circuit. This can cause serious problems with more complex sets, especially at higher frequencies.

Another, much cheaper, technique is to use a piece of wood with drawing pins pushed in to it to hold the wires. Instead of drawing pins, brass screws and screwcups can be used (Figure 3.4), the wires being trapped under the edge of the screw cups. It is possible to build some fairly complex receivers using this method, but they tend to be rather large. Also, any dampness in the wood provides high resistance paths for current between different parts of the circuit.

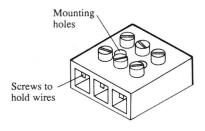

Figure 3.5

Finally, you can use terminal blocks (Figure 3.5) screwed to a wooden baseboard.

Techniques using soldering

For long term reliable performance you really need to solder the circuit together. So, let us look at how to solder.

Tinning the bit
This is done to *all* new bits before use and also occasionally throughout the life of the bit. Allow the iron to heat up, and after a few minutes wipe the bit with a damp cloth. Then bring the end of a length of solder to the bit, and allow the solder to flow all over the bit. Wipe the bit with the damp cloth, and repeat the process until the bit is shiny all over.

Making the joint
The surfaces to be joined should be clean – rub conductors with fine emery paper or scrape with a craft knife – and free from grease. Any bare copper wires should be tinned before soldering by applying the hot bit to the wire and allowing solder to flow over the wire. Most component leads are pre-tinned, and so will not require this treatment. Wherever possible, ensure that there is a strong mechanical joint before soldering the joint, either by twisting the wires together, or wrapping a wire around a terminal, etc. See later for special techniques used when soldering components into printed circuits or Veroboard.

Apply the hot bit to the joint, and apply the solder to the heated joint, *not* the bit. The solder will flow over the joint, and the bit and solder can be removed. Do not apply too much solder, as this can lead to 'blobby' joints which look untidy and can cause short circuits to other parts of the circuit, especially if the circuit has components close together. *Do not* move the joint until the solder has set. Assuming the bit was hot enough, and that the joint was clean, a good joint will be made in less than about 6 seconds. Longer than this indicates that the iron was not hot enough or that the joint was dirty. During the building of circuits, wipe the bit occasionally with a damp cloth to clean it.

Do not overheat the joint or you may find your components have been damaged!

Soldering problems

A good joint is shiny, with solder spread smoothly all over the joint concerned. If the solder has not spread over the joint, then it indicates that there could be some grease or dirt causing problems. A grey, grainy looking joint is called a *dry joint*, and is often caused by moving the leads in the joint before the solder has set. Alternatively, it can be caused by applying solder to the joint before the joint has been heated sufficiently.

After some use, small craters known as *pits* may start appearing in the bit. If this occurs, then a new bit is needed.

In some cases, you may see traces of flux around completed joints. This can be removed, purely for appearance's sake, with an old toothbrush.

As a general rule-of-thumb, passive components, e.g. resistors, capacitors, should be soldered into circuit before active components, e.g. transistors, integrated circuits. This reduces risk of damage by heat to the more heat-sensitive active components.

Tag strips

This is a tried and trusted method of soldered construction, in which components are soldered to metal tags fixed to an insulating strip (Figure 3.6). The strip can then be mounted on the chassis with nuts and bolts.

This method is not much good when it comes to using integrated circuit (IC) packages, as the pins on these devices would be too close together to allow them to be soldered. To use ICs, constructors tend to build using either printed circuit boards or Veroboard.

Veroboard construction

Veroboard is an insulating board with holes in it either 0.1 in or 0.15 in apart. Use the 0.1 in board, as this will take integrated circuit packages directly. It comes in two types: plain, where the components are pushed

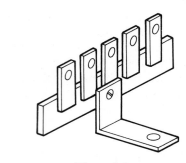

Figure 3.6

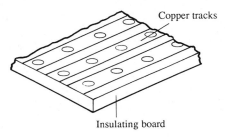

Figure 3.7

through the board from one side and joined on the other side by wires, or copper clad, where one side of the board has copper strips or tracks on it, linking holes. These strips or tracks form conductors (Figure 3.7), and components are soldered to them to make up circuits. Breaks can be made in the tracks if required and wire links may be made to other strips. Generally, constructional details will show where a break is to be made – by, say, an 'X' in the component layout (the method used in this book). Veroboard comes in a variety of sizes and a hacksaw can be used to cut a piece from a larger sheet.

Breaks are cut in the strip using a device called a spot face cutter, available from most component stockists. When soldering, take care not to overheat the copper as it will peel off if you do!

Printed circuit boards
Printed circuit boards (PCBs) are universally used in manufactured electronic equipment, and whilst it is possible for the amateur to produce them it can be quite involved, especially for one-off circuits. PCBs

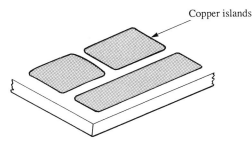

Copper islands

Figure 3.8

start life as an insulating board with copper on one side. Double-sided PCB, i.e. with copper on both sides is also available, but not usually used by the amateur. The connections between components may be drawn on the copper using either a special pen or a rub-down transfer. The excess copper, not needed for connections, is then removed chemically, holes are drilled and the components pushed through from the non-copper side and soldered in, using similar techniques to those employed when soldering components into Veroboard. Simple PCBs can be made using a technique called island PCB construction. Here, large areas of copper are left for connections to be made to and copper between these islands is removed to allow each island to be insulated from the rest. Components are then soldered to the copper islands without holes, thus simplifying the job (Figure 3.8).

PCB kits are available which give full instructions on how to make your own printed circuit boards. However, none of the circuits in this book uses a PCB – Veroboard and tagstrips are the order of the day.

General considerations

Good connections
Most circuit problems are due to bad connections. Wires oxidise when exposed to the air, and so should be cleaned before being joined together. They can be rubbed clean with fine emery paper or a *hard* eraser, or gently scraped clean with a craft knife. A good mechanical joint, formed by twisting the wires together, is a good idea, even when soldering. The rules about cleaning wires also apply to Veroboard tracks and printed circuit board connections.

A good idea when soldering connecting leads onto Veroboard or

PCB is to use pins, previously soldered into the board. These allow connections to be made to the board after it has been fixed into position.

Mechanical strength
Components should be mounted so that they cannot move. Movement can cause problems in tuning receivers, and may even prevent the sets concerned from working at all!

Layout
In some circuits, the physical position of components with respect to each other can cause problems. For example, an audio output transformer close to a tuned circuit could detune the circuit or induce voltages in it which will prevent correct operation of the receiver.

As a rule-of-thumb, output and input parts of circuits should be kept apart; there is much to be said for having the aerial circuits of the receiver on the left of the circuit board and the output stage on the right of the circuit board. In extreme cases, metal screens can be placed around susceptible parts of the circuit. Screens should be earthed by connecting to the 0 V line of the receiver.

Stray coupling
It is possible for stray capacitive or inductive coupling to occur between adjacent parts of a circuit. This is particularly so if we have long wires crossing the circuit board. One trick here is to keep wires as short as possible, and use screened wire, such as thin coaxial cable, for certain parts of the circuit. Coupling can be caused by Veroboard or printed circuit board tracks running close to both input and output stages of the equipment.

Decoupling
It is usual to connect capacitors across the power supply lines of equipment to prevent radio frequency (RF) or audio frequency (AF) signals being circulated throughout the equipment. Typically, electrolytics of around 100 μF are used to bypass AF to ground, and a small capacitor of say, 47 nF, can be used to bypass RF to ground. The electrolytic capacitor should, in theory, be able to do this latter job, but they are not very efficient at RF. Poor decoupling can lead to instability, or the set not working at all in extreme conditions. Figure 3.9 illustrates some

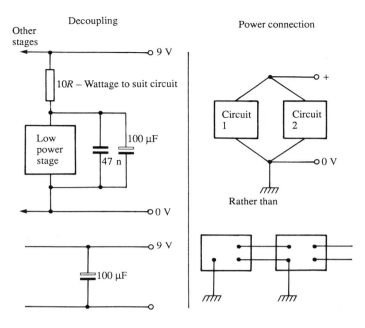

Figure 3.9

decoupling methods, and the correct way to arrange the power supply connections to circuit boards.

Front panels

Some components, when fixed to a metal front panel, will make electrical connection with that panel and so put the panel at the same voltage level as the component concerned. A typical example is a variable capacitor, where the frame of the component will be connected to the panel. This is an occasional source of unexpected short circuits, particularly if jack sockets, etc. are also mounted on the panel.

Polarity of components

As we saw in Chapter 1, some components *must* be connected a certain way round in circuits to work. These components can be permanently damaged if connected incorrectly. Figure 3.10 shows different methods used to mark the positive ends of components.

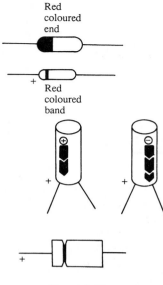

Figure 3.10

Power supplies

All the circuits in this book use batteries. Do not use battery eliminator circuits, as they can often cause noise which will degrade the perform-ance of the receivers. In addition, batteries are much safer!

We can now start building! The simplest circuit to look at is some-thing called a crystal set, which does not even use a battery!

FOUR

Crystal sets

The crystal set is the oldest type of receiver, and the cheapest to run, requiring no power except for that which it extracts from the signals it receives! For this reason, it is a popular first project for radio hobbyists. In addition, building crystal sets can teach us a great deal about some basics of radio, such as the importance of aerials, selectivity and sensitivity, soldering and the influence of the time of day and year on the signals likely to be received.

Figure 4.1 shows a circuit diagram of a crystal set. It can be split into 4 main parts:

1 The tuned circuit

This uses the properties of the LC circuits we examined in Chapter 1 to select one signal from the many that will impinge on the aerial. A good aerial, incidentally, is essential for crystal sets. The tuned circuit usually consists of a variable capacitor and a fixed value inductor. The circuit is tuned by varying the capacity of the variable capacitor as was discussed in Chapter 1. The values of capacitor and coil used depend upon the frequencies of interest. This constitutes the RF stage of this receiver – the part of the set that processes the radio frequency signals.

2 The detector

This stage uses a germanium diode to demodulate, or detect, the incoming radio wave. The output signal is a varying electrical voltage which carries the sound information of the received signal. Diodes which can be used here include the OA81 or OA91.

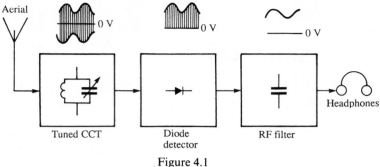

Figure 4.1

3 The RF filter

This capacitor passes any radio frequency signals still present to earth. This is particularly important if the output from the crystal set is going to be boosted up by an audio amplifier, as RF signals reaching the amplifier could lead to instability. Values up to about 0.01 μF will work here.

4 The audio output

The output from a crystal set as described is at a very high impedance, and low level, so is capable of directly driving only high impedance headphones.

An impedance matching transformer is often used to allow low impedance (say, 8 ohm) headphones to be used. A suitable transformer is the LT700 type, though any transformer designed for matching a high impedance circuit to a low impedance circuit will work.

Crystal earpieces are available, and these have a very high impedance and so can be connected directly to the diode output, thus allowing us to dispense with the transformer. However, these earpieces often give disappointing results. Should you wish to try a crystal earpiece, then a high value resistor – say, a few hundred kilohms – needs to be connected across the earpiece: this is to provide a leakage path for the RF decoupling capacitor, and will improve performance with such an earpiece.

Disadvantages of the crystal set

It is the simplicity of the crystal set that causes the problems. There are four main failings.

The first is that the output signals are quite faint, even with a good aerial, and are only suitable for headphone reception. This is due to the lack of amplification in the receiver, and can be alleviated by adding a small audio amplifier.

Second, the crystal set cannot resolve very faint signals. This is because the RF signal is not amplified before demodulation and the diode detector requires signals of a reasonable voltage level before it will demodulate them. Germanium diodes can detect smaller signals than silicon diodes, and so are used in crystal sets in preference to the silicon devices. The ability of a receiver of any type to convert faint signals into a readable audio output is called the *sensitivity* of a receiver. The crystal set has poor sensitivity.

The third disadvantage of the crystal set lies in its inability to separate two or more strongish signals that are close to one another in frequency. This ability is called the *selectivity* of a receiver. A selective receiver is one that can separate two strongish signals within a few kilohertz of each other. The poor selectivity of the crystal set is due to the simple nature of the tuned circuit, and the loading applied to the tuned circuit by the diode and the aerial. Anything connected to a tuned circuit will load it by taking some energy out of it. The effect of loading is to damp a tuned circuit, as seen in Figure 4.2.

The selectivity depends upon the Q of the tuned circuit. A high Q circuit loses as little signal as possible, and to achieve this the electrical resistance of the coil must be as low as possible, good quality capacitors must be used, and the tuned circuit should only be lightly loaded. The

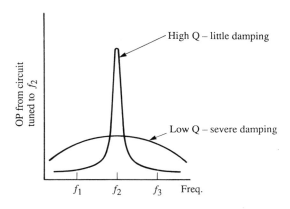

Figure 4.2

selectivity of crystal sets can be improved by reducing the loading and increasing the Q, but it is still poor when compared with more sophisticated equipment. Selectivity can also be improved by having more than one tuned circuit in a receiver.

In extreme cases, strong signals may well be untunable, and appear in the background of all other received stations. This is a symptom of *overloading*.

Finally, due to the simplicity of the diode detector, crystal sets are only able to demodulate AM signals. CW and SSB are not resolvable using a simple diode detector as shown here. This is not a great drawback, however, because crystal sets are rarely sensitive enough to receive such signals.

Building a crystal set

Figure 4.3 shows the circuit and construction details for a very simple crystal set, capable of receiving signals in the medium wave broadcast band. Variable capacitor VC1 is a 365 pF air spaced tuning capacitor, Jackson Type O or similar. This will be useful in other projects as well, so although it is a little expensive it can be re-used. Alternatively, you may feel like experimenting with variable capacitors from old receivers; anything with a maximum capacity of between 365 pF and 500 pF will work.

Winding the coil

Pre-wound coils are available to tune the medium waveband, but tend to be designed for use in more complex receivers. Crystal set coils must have the following characteristics:

1 as low an electrical resistance as possible – to give as high a Q as possible. This can be done by winding the coil on a ferrite rod to increase the coil inductance without using too much wire.

2 a tapped coil – to ensure the tuned circuit is loaded as lightly as possible by the diode and the aerial. This involves providing connections at each end of the coil *and* at points between the coil ends. Anything connected to these taps will still load the coil, but the loading will be reduced.

The coil is wound with 36 swg enamelled wire as shown in Figure 4.3b. The card cylinder slides up and down the ferrite rod and

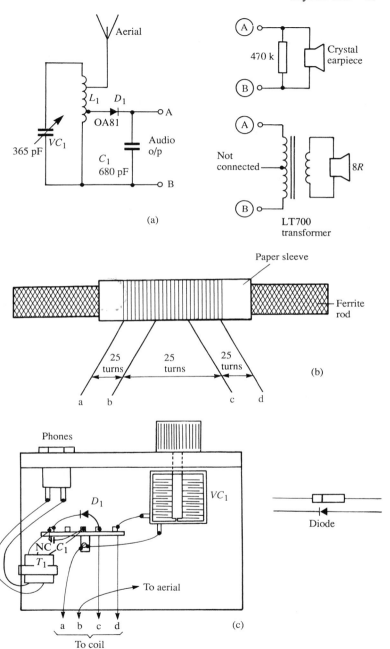

Figure 4.3

allows us to vary the inductance of the coil to suit the value of VC_1. Positioning the winding towards the centre of the ferrite rod will increase the coil inductance, whilst positioning it at the end of the rod will decrease the inductance. The winding consists of 75 turns, with tapping points at 25 and 50 turns. Use tape to fix the wire at each end of the winding. Gently remove the enamel from the wire ends and tapping points with fine sandpaper, taking care not to break the wire at the tapping points. Then tin the bared ends with solder.

The set is built on a chassis made from an aluminium box. Two large holes need to be drilled in the front panel, one for the shaft of the tuning control and one for the headphone socket. In addition, you will need smaller holes to attach the variable capacitor to the front panel, attach the terminal strip to the chassis and to fix the chassis and front panel together. Figure 4.3c shows the way in which the components are connected together. Take care when soldering the diode not to overheat it. Another point to note is that the moving plates of the variable capacitor will be electrically connected to the chassis. A similar situation occurs with the headphone socket; one terminal will be connected to the chassis. The headphones used are common 8 ohm stereo 'phones. You will also need a converter plug to allow the stereo phones to give mono output.

Testing the receiver

To test the receiver, connect up an aerial comprising of a length of wire – the longer the better – and plug in the headphones. Position the coil towards one end of the ferrite rod, and tune the set. You should hear at least one station, though you may need to move the coil along the ferrite rod to change the tuning range in some areas. Once you have got a station try connecting a length of wire to the earth terminal to see if it gives any improvement in signal strength. In Sheffield, the prototype set received two local radio stations, as well as Radio 2 and Radio 1. You may find that the set overloads on strong signals, demonstrating the poor selectivity, even with the use of tapping points on the coil. The poor sensitivity will also be apparent, as will the low level of the signals in the headphones. You might like to try increasing the set's selectivity by decreasing the aerial length or by connecting a low value (less than 100 pF) capacitor connected between the aerial and the aerial terminal. Both of these actions will decrease the loading of the aerial on the tuned circuit.

Improving the simple crystal set

The easiest improvement is a small battery powered audio amplifier which increases the volume of the stations we can hear, in turn increasing the number of stations that are audible. A crystal set incorporating a simple amplifier is shown in Figure 4.4a. In addition to the amplifier, the way in which the diode and aerial are connected to the set has been changed. Rather than tappings, transformer coupling is used which improves the selectivity of the set by decreasing the loading on the tuned circuit formed by L_{1a} and VC_1. The new coil is shown in Figure 4.4b.

The LM380 integrated circuit requires only a few additional components to make a useful audio amplifier. R_1, C_1, C_2 and C_3 form a simple filter to prevent entry of RF signals to the audio amplifier. If this were to happen, the amplifier may become unstable and produce horrible noises rather than an amplified radio station! R_2, C_4, C_5 and C_7 are also to prevent instability, and it is important to connect pins 3, 4, 5 and 10, 11, 12 of the LM380 to 0 volts for the same reason. Pins 7 and 14 of the chip are the power connections and pin 2 is an input connection. The circuit can be built on a piece of Veroboard, the component layout of which is shown in Figure 4.4c. Do not solder the IC directly into circuit, this may damage it if excess heat is used: instead, first solder in a 14-pin DIL socket and simply push the IC into circuit. A socket has the added advantage that it allows you to use the LM380 again. Break the tracks on the Veroboard where indicated, and follow the advice given in Chapter 3 for soldering. A PP3 battery provides sufficient power for the circuit, and should be connected to the circuit with a PP3 battery clip – the red lead of the clip is connected to the positive terminal of the battery. The loudspeaker used can be of any physical size, and larger ones will give better results. Alternatively, headphones can still be used.

Testing the amplifier

Connect the battery. You should hear a click and a hissing noise if all is well. Touching pin 2 should produce a buzzing noise. Place your finger on the LM380 and, if it is hot, disconnect the battery and check your wiring!

Now connect the amplifier to the crystal set. Connect the battery. On tuning the set you should hear the stations previously heard, but at a greater volume. In addition, there will probably be a few more sta-

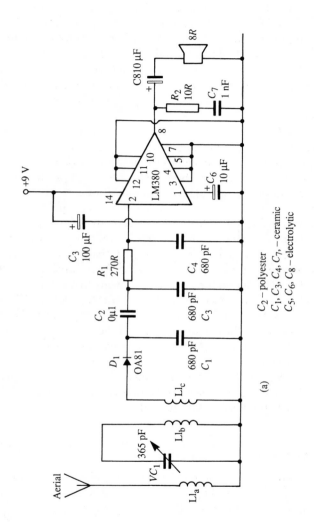

C_2 – polyester
C_1, C_3, C_4, C_7, – ceramic
C_5, C_6, C_8 – electrolytic

(a)

Figure 4.4

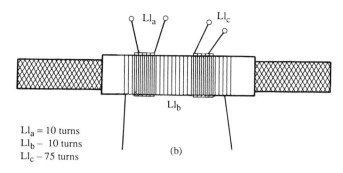

$Ll_a = 10$ turns
$Ll_b - 10$ turns
$Ll_c - 75$ turns

(b)

Viewed from component side

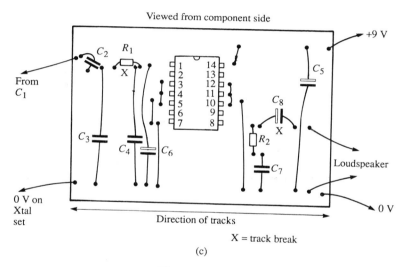

X = track break

(c)

Figure 4.4 (cont.)

tions audible as well. The set is more prone to overloading, and a shorter aerial will work – experiment and see!

On to the short waves

It is possible to get a crystal set to work on the short waves, though the results are not very good. Figure 4.5 shows a simple short wave crystal set with which you might like to experiment. The tuned circuit allows reception between about 5.5 and 10 MHz. The receiver needs a decent aerial, but selectivity and sensitivity are both poor. The prototype set

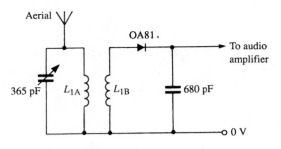

L_{1A} – 20 turns
L_{1B} – 15 turns over 'earthy' end of L_{1A}
$L_{IA, B}$ wound on toilet roll core. 4.4 cm in diameter

Figure 4.5

received signals from all over Europe, and will demonstrate the fact that the reception of short wave radio signals depends upon the time of day and season. You will also see that transmissions on the short wave bands are more prone to fading and distortion than the medium wave signals we first received. Due to poor selectivity, and the sheer number of stations on SW, it is unlikely that you will hear just one station at once. However, by persevering you will be able to pick several of the stronger international broadcasts up, and get a taste of short wave listening.

FIVE

Regenerative receivers

A few experiments with crystal sets will soon reveal that something better is required. We have seen how an audio amplifier can increase the volume of stations received, but it does little to increase the sensitivity or selectivity of the receiver. A quantum leap in performance can be obtained by using a more complex type of receiver called the *regenerative* receiver. In this type of set the incoming RF signals are amplified prior to detection, thus increasing sensitivity, by a circuit which also increases the selectivity of the receiver. In addition to this increase in selectivity and sensitivity, the regenerative set can also demodulate CW and SSB signals. A regenerative receiver is an example of what is known as a *straight receiver*. In these sets, all amplification of the RF signal is done at the frequency of the incoming signal. Thus if we are listening to a signal on 6000 kHz, all RF amplification is carried out at 6000 kHz before the signal is detected and turned into audio signals (Figure 5.1).

The RF stages of a regenerative receiver also double as detectors of the RF signal, this being possible due to the non-linear behaviour of most simple amplifier circuits. At the heart of any regenerative receiver is an RF amplifier, so we will start to examine how these sets work by looking at an RF amplifier (Figure 5.2).

Variable capacitor coil VC_1 and coil L_1 tune the frequency in which we are interested, and C_1 links the RF signal to the gate of the FET. A field effect transistor is used to reduce the loading applied to the tuned circuit and so increase the receiver's selectivity. R_1, R_2 and C_2 set the operating conditions of the FET amplifier, and RFC_1 provides a load across which the RF output signal can develop. The output signal is larger than the input, and is also 180° out of phase with the input. This phase shift is characteristic of many single stage amplifiers.

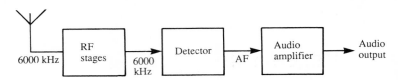

Figure 5.1

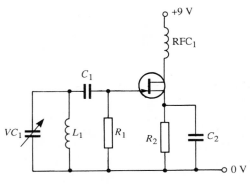

Figure 5.2

Although this circuit will amplify the radio frequency signals and provide some degree of detection, it is not yet a regenerative detector stage. Regeneration – occasionally still known by its older name, reaction – is a technique whereby part of the output signal is fed back to the input of the amplifier, in phase with incoming signals. This positive feedback reinforces the input signal, vastly increasing the effective gain of the circuit. In addition, selectivity of the circuit is increased because the tuned circuit Q is increased by the regenerative action. Detection of AM signals is also enhanced.

Positive feedback needs to be controlled, however; too much and the receiver will burst into oscillation at the frequency to which it is tuned. To produce a regenerative detector circuit, then, we need the following elements:

1 an RF amplifier

2 a means of providing positive feedback in the circuit. This must ensure the signal fed back is in the same phase as the input signal, and so will often require some means of reversing the phase of the output signal

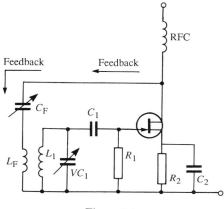

Figure 5.3

3 a means of controlling the amount of positive feedback applied.

Figure 5.3 satisfies these three statements. Capacitor C_F provides feedback control, while coil L_F provides the phase reversal and the feedback, by inducing a voltage in L_1. The connections to L_F need to be made so that the voltages in L_1 are in phase with the radio frequency voltages from the aerial. If L_F is phased incorrectly, the voltages induced will cancel out the signals from the aerial, thus decreasing gain. This negative feedback will increase losses in the circuit, decrease the Q of the circuit and so lead to loss of selectivity as well as sensitivity. Should the phasing of L_F be incorrect, then it is a simple matter of reversing the connections to the coil in order to correct this problem.

In a regenerative receiver, applying too much feedback will cause oscillation. Maximum sensitivity and selectivity occurs just below the point at which oscillation starts – the *threshold of oscillation* – and it is at this point that AM signals are demodulated. CW and SSB signals, on the other hand, are demodulated with the set adjusted so as to be just *above* the threshold of oscillation. In this state, for SSB, the oscillation produced by the regenerative detector, at the frequency of the received signal, replaces the carrier wave of the SSB signal removed at transmission, and so renders the signal readable. For CW, it provides a signal which beats with the incoming CW signal to render it audible as a series of tones.

The amount of feedback required to keep the set at the threshold of oscillation depends upon the received frequency, and in practical

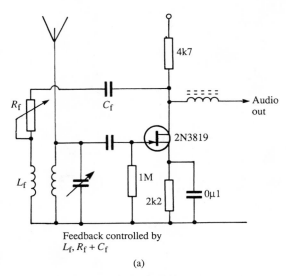

Feedback controlled by
$L_f, R_f + C_f$

(a)

Figure 5.4(a)

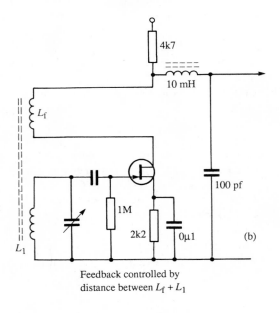

Feedback controlled by
distance between $L_f + L_1$

Figure 5.4(b)

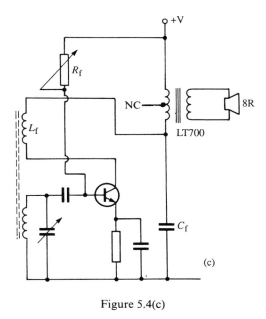

Figure 5.4(c)

receivers this means the amount of feedback supplied must be adjustable. Figure 5.4 shows some theoretical regenerative detector stages.

A medium wave regenerative receiver

You will learn an awful lot about regenerative sets by building and using them, and some excellent results will be obtained even with simple aerials. This receiver is almost classical in its design, as it is a semiconductor equivalent of early valve regenerative receivers. Figure 5.5 shows the circuit for this receiver; despite appearances, it is quite a simple circuit to get up and running!

Let us see how the set works; it is split into three sections, the regenerative detector, the RF filter and the audio amplifier. C_6 and C_7 are decoupling components to shunt any RF on the positive supply rail to earth. R_1 and R_2 bias the field effect transistor, and C_2 provides a route to earth for any audio signals on the FET drain. The FET has a very high input impedance, thus loading on the tuned circuit (L_2/VC_1) is minimised. The load of the FET is split into two parts; the 10 mH choke allows audio signals through, but acts as a load for the RF

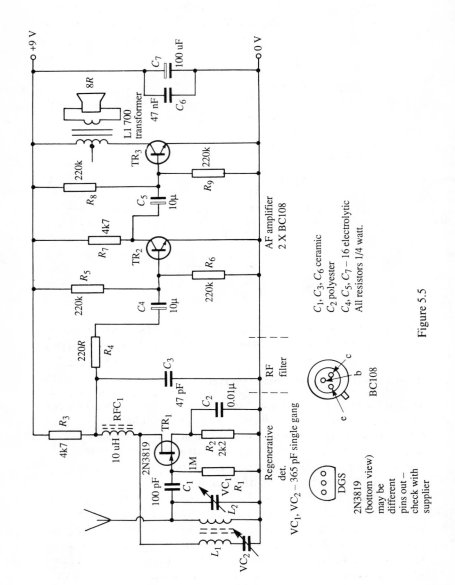

Figure 5.5

signals, and these are effectively diverted through the feedback system (VC_2/L_1). The audio load is the 4k7 resistor, and from here the audio signal is taken to the AF amplifier via the RF filter formed by R_4 and C_3. The 47 pF capacitor shunts any RF to earth, but has a negligible effect on AF signals. A simple two stage amplifier is used to drive a loudspeaker or headphones; the LT700 transformer converts the high impedance signal provided by the BC108 transistor into a low impedance signal capable of driving 8 Ω headphones.

Building the receiver

Figure 5.6 shows the component layout for the reciver. Build the set 'backwards', i.e. starting with the audio amplifier stage, and test each stage as it is completed. Follow the advice given in Chapter 3 regarding construction, and use pins for coil connections. To test the audio amplifier stage; plug in headphones, and apply power. A click should be heard, and touching the positive end of C_4 will produce a buzz in the headphones.

Now solder in the components of the RF filter, and once completed test, in a similar manner, by touching the junction of C_3 and R_4, again listening for a buzz.

Finally, the regenerative detector, without the aerial coil, can be built. The frames of the two variable capacitors should be connected to the 0 V line in each case, as the frames will be connected to each other by the metal front panel. Even if a metal panel is not used, it is still a good idea to connect the frames to 0 volts. Once construction is complete, *check everything* before going any further. When you are happy, apply power. Bringing your finger near the FET should cause a buzz now, if this occurs the chances are that the FET amplifier is functioning.

Now wind the coil and connect it up.

The coil

The MW coil used in the crystal set is suitable, though we have to wind an extra coil to fit on the ferrite rod to act as the regeneration winding. This can be about 6 turns wound on a cylinder made of thin card so that it can slide up and down the ferrite rod. There should be enough play in the leads of this coil to allow it to be slipped off the end of the ferrite rod and replaced the other way round if you find the phasing is

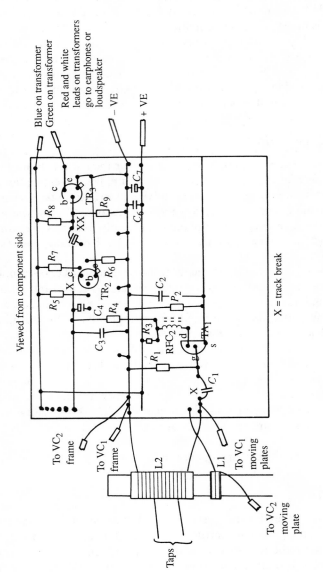

— represent tracks on the other side of the board

Viewed from component side

Blue on transformer
Green on transformer

Red and white
leads on transformers
go to earphones or
loudspeaker

− VE

+ VE

X = track break

To VC_2 frame

To VC_1 frame

L2

L1

To VC_1 moving plates

To VC_2 moving plate

Taps

Figure 5.6

not correct. The coil is connected up to the circuit as shown in Figure 5.6. Position the aerial winding towards one end of the ferrite rod and the regeneration winding at the other end.

Testing the receiver

Connect up an aerial – a few metres of wire will do, the longer the better – and adjust regeneration control VC_2 so that it is about half meshed. Connect up the phones and battery and try tuning in a station. If nothing is heard, try meshing the regeneration control further to increase the regeneration, or moving the regeneration coil closer to the aerial coil. Once a station is found, slowly increasing the regeneration will cause the volume of the station in the headphones to increase until the set starts oscillating, when a whistle will be heard. Now, carefully turn the regeneration control back a little until the station is heard loud and clear. If you cannot attain oscillation at any position of the coil or regneration control, the phasing of regeneration coil L_2 may not be correct. Slip the coil off the ferrite rod, reverse it and put it on again. Now repeat the above procedure, and find a position of the coil as far along the ferrite rod as possible from the aerial coil that will allow you to use the regeneration control to bring the set into oscillation at any position of the tuning control. Once this position is found, glue the regeneration coil into place.

Operating the set

Operating a regenerative set is a little awkward at first, but practice does make perfect. These instructions are valid for the MW set just built and the SW version to be described later.

AM reception

Tune the set to a signal, turn up the regeneration until oscillation *just* starts and then turn the regeneration control back a little until the station is heard clearly and without any distortion. The set is now at its most sensitive.

An alternative method is to turn up the regeneration until oscillation just starts (in the absence of a signal, the hiss gets louder) and then tune for signals. This is a particularly useful procedure when searching for faint signals. A station will announce its presence by causing a beat note to be heard as it is tuned through. Tune for the maximum whistle, then back off the regeneration control a little. Slight retuning may then be required.

SSB and CW

On short wave, you are likely to hear amateur broadcasts using SSB or CW which are resolved when the receiver is just oscillating. SSB reception sounds a little odd ('Donald Duck talking into a drain pipe' is one expression I have heard) unless precisely tuned, and for tuning the amateur bands with a simple set like this some sort of *bandspreading* will be needed (see later). Too much oscillation will decrease the sensitivity and selectivity of the receiver, and the optimum position for SSB and CW resolution is only just beyond the threshold of oscillation.

The setting of the regeneration control will vary from frequency to frequency, and so will need regular adjustment when tuning to keep the set at its most sensitive.

Problems and enhancements

1 No regeneration over part or whole of tuning range
Assuming the phasing of the regeneration coil is correct, and you have positioned it close enough to the aerial coil, the following suggestions may help:

(a) reduce the value of R_2, to a minimum of about $270\,\Omega$
(b) the aerial may be dampening the tuned circuit and reducing regeneration – see section on *aerial linkage*, later
(c) is the battery flat?
(d) check components and wiring again, particularly around the generation control and coil
(e) use a $500\,\text{pF}$ capacitor for the regeneration control instead of a $365\,\text{pF}$ unit
(f) try another FET. I have tried 2N3819, MPF102 and E5555 units in the circuit and they have all worked.

2 Regeneration can not be controlled over all or part of tuning range

(a) regeneration coil too close to aerial coil. Move it further away slightly

(b) too many turns on regeneration coil. Take a couple of turns off
(c) increase the value of R_2
(d) check components and wiring again.

3 Backlash on tuning or regeneration
When using either of the variable capacitors, there may be a small lack
of response when first tuned from rest. This is called backlash, a form
of mechanical hysterisis, and can cause problems when tuning or
applying regeneration

(a) check that the mechanical construction of the set is rigid, particularly the mounting of the variable capacitors and their control
knobs
(b) sometimes, a form of electrical backlash may be experienced when
the regeneration and aerial coils are too close together or there are
too many turns on the regeneration winding. This causes difficulty
in adjusting the receiver to the sensitive point just below the threshold of oscillation. Cure as for (2) above.

4 Bandspread tuning
When tuning the receiver, especially at the threshold of oscillation, the
selectivity of the receiver can make tuning very 'tight', with stations so
close together it is impossible to resolve them individually, especially
on the short waves. What is required is a means of 'spreading out' the
tuning, so that a larger turn of the tuning knob will cover a smaller
range of frequencies. This is called *bandspreading*, and there are two
main ways of achieving it:

(a) mechanical bandspreading. Here, a device called a *slow motion
drive* is used to gear down the rotation of the tuning control so that,
say, eight turns of the tuning control are needed to traverse the full
tuning range. These slow motion drives are available from component stockists listed in the Appendix 1. A ratio of 6:1 or 8:1 is quite
adequate for our needs. The drives also come with a vernier scaled
dial, making logging of stations easier. A diagram showing how
such a dial is connected to a tuning control is given in Figure 5.7.
Mechanical bandspreading has the advantage of using only one
tuning control, though trying to quickly tune from one end of the
tuning scale to the other is slow!
(b) electrical bandspreading. A smaller value variable capacitor can be
connected in parallel with the main tuning control, as shown in

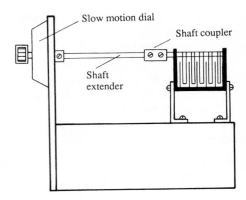

Figure 5.7

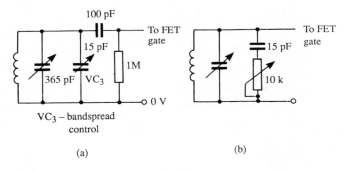

Figure 5.8

Figure 5.8a. VC_3 is the bandspread control, and may be mounted on the front panel of the receiver. In use, it is set to be about half-meshed, and the main tuning control, often referred to as a *bandset* control, is used to roughly tune the desired station. VC_3 is then adjusted for best results.

Another arrangement, using a variable resistor, is shown in Figure 5.8b; this is cheaper but not as effective.

5 Hand capacitance
Another phenomenon associated with simple sets with good selectivity is called *hand capacity*. Here, the proximity of an earthy object, typically the user's hand on the tuning control, can affect the tuning of the

receiver. When the hand is removed, the set detunes slightly, often losing the station being listened to!

With sets built on metal chassis, the easiest solution is to attach a few metres of wire to the earth terminal of the receiver. You often don't even need to connect it to earth. This should either totally remove the effect or reduce it to acceptable levels.

Alternatively, the variable capacitors suffering from this problem can be mounted some distance behind the front panel and linked to their control knobs with extension shafts made of insulating materials such as plastic, nylon or wooden dowel (the mounting arrangement would be similar to that in Figure 5.7).

6 Aerial linkage
The coupling of the aerial to a regenerative set can have great effects on the receiver, causing oscillation to cease or selectivity and sensitivity to decrease. Ideally, the coupling of aerial to receiver is a matter of compromise; enough signal must get into the receiver for good reception but coupling must be loose enough to allow regeneration to work smoothly. Figure 5.9 shows a variety of ways of coupling the aerial to the MW receiver just described. In Figure 5.9 an extra winding on the

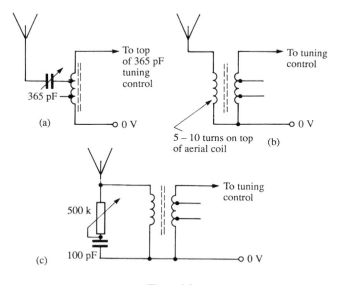

Figure 5.9

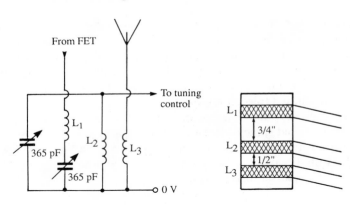

L$_1$, L$_2$ + L$_3$ wound cardboard or
plastic cylinder 1.75 in. in diameter

L$_1$ = 6 turns 36 swg wire – regeneration coil
L$_2$ = 8 turns 36 swg wire – tuning coil
L$_3$ = 12 turns 36 swg wire – aerial link coil

Figure 5.10

coil is needed: this can be a few turns of insulated wire over the top of the aerial winding. These coupling methods can be especially useful with long aerials.

A short wave regenerative receiver

The MW set that we have just built can be easily adapted to short wave reception. All that is required is a new coil (details shown in Figure 5.10), and some means of bandspread is virtually essential, especially if you are considering using the receiver for receiving SSB or CW transmissions. Once the coil is wound and connected, the receiver can be tested like the MW set. If regeneration is too fierce, move the regeneration winding a little away from the tuned coil; if regeneration cannot be obtained over the full tuning range, move it a little closer to the winding. The aerial coupling coil allows you to connect a long aerial directly to the receiver without too much loading; increasing the number of turns on this winding will increase the strength of stations heard, but will also increase the chance of overloading the receiver. As described, this coil will allow the receiver to tune from about 3.5 MHz to about 9.8 MHz, and in this range you will find the 60 m, 49 m, 41 m and 31 m broadcast bands and the 80 and 40 m amateur bands, though care in operation is required to get good results on the two amateur bands. You might like to try re-winding the tuning coil to change the receiver's coverage. If you do this, you may also have to change the regeneration winding and the aerial coupling winding – regenerative sets are great for experimenting with!

You are likely to find hand capacitance a bigger problem on short wave, and if you wind coils for quite high frequencies – 20 to 30 MHz – you will find this effect very noticeable. The simple techniques described above will cure the problem.

Once you have got the simple SW receiver working, you may wish to experiment with different designs. You might like to get one of the regenerative detectors shown in Figure 5.4 to work, or try out designs from some of the books listed in Appendix 3.

SIX

Direct conversion receivers

If you have built the regenerative receiver described in the last chapter then you will probably agree that it is *operated* rather than just used! The tuning and regeneration controls interact with each other, and adjustment of the receiver for CW or SSB reception can be a little fiddly to say the least! In addition, the regenerative receiver is overloaded fairly easily, and selectivity depends to a great extent upon the setting of the regeneration control.

Nowadays, listeners who concentrate on receiving signals from amateur radio stations on home-made equipment tend to use a type of set called the *direct conversion receiver*, or DC receiver. This set is specially designed to receive SSB or CW transmissions, though it can detect AM broadcasts with a little care. A block diagram of a simple DC receiver is shown in Figure 6.1. As can be seen, there are two tuning controls, although in some sets the tuned RF stage between aerial and mixer stage is often left as a fixed frequency, fairly low Q tuned circuit. Tuning is carried out by adjusting variable frequency oscillator (VFO) frequency, and where front end tuning is variable it is used to 'peak up' the desired signal.

The DC receiver depends on the principle of mixing. In Chapter 2, we saw how two AC signals can interact in such a way as to give us sum and difference signals as well as the original two AC signals. In the DC receiver, one signal that is to be mixed comes from the aerial, and the other comes from an RF oscillator tuned to a frequecy that is very close to that of the desired signal. A few minutes thought here will indicate that the difference signal will be a very low frequency signal indeed – a few kHz or even less. For example, imagine a CW station on 3.545 MHz, and imagine the local oscillator circuit tuned to 3.546 Mhz. Here, the difference signal would be 1 kHz, well within the range of

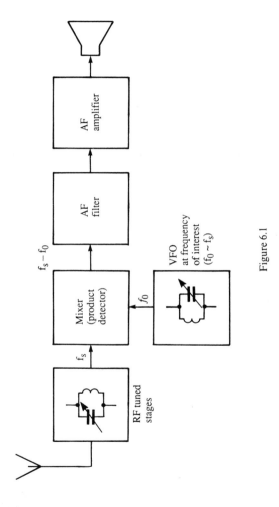

$f_s - f_0$

AF
amplifier

AF
filter

f_s

Mixer
(product
detector)

f_0

RF tuned
stages

VFO
at frequency
of interest
$(f_0 \sim f_s)$

Figure 6.1

signals that we could amplify and turn into sound. This process is called *product detection* and will allow SSB and CW signals to be demodulated. The demodulated signal is passed through the AF filter and then is amplified to loudspeaker or headphone strength.

DC receivers are also known as *homodyne* receivers. Although AM reception is possible, the oscillator frequency must be exactly that of the received signal as, otherwise, a beat note will be heard. Indeed, even when the two frequencies *are* the same, AM reception on DC receivers may still suffer a warbling effect on the received audio. This is called *growling* and is caused by phase differences between the oscillator signal and the received radio signal. To get rid of this, the oscillator signal must match the incoming signal in frequency *and* phase. This is called *phase locking* and the oscillator in such a receiver is said to be phase locked to the incoming signal – not an easy task. Such a receiver is called a *synchrodyne* receiver and is rather beyond the scope of this book. Synchrodyne techniques are also required when attempting to resolve RTTY or NBFM with a DC receiver.

The product detector

The important part of a DC receiver as far as we are concerned is the product detector circuit. Four typical circuits are shown in Figure 6.2. The oscillator input is always much larger than the signal with which it will be mixed, and is easily generated by an oscillator which is usually followed by a single transistor buffer stage to prevent tuning of the front end tuned circuit from altering oscillator tuning in an effect called *pulling*. The mixer stage should be linear for best results, and so it is important that the stage is not overloaded, and hence driven into non-linearity by the input signals. As can be seen from the above diagrams, a variety of semiconductor devices can be used as mixers; diodes and MOSFETs being particularly popular devices. Although special diodes called *hot carrier* diodes are often used at higher frequencies, I have found that germanium diodes like the OA91 will work on the 160 and 80 m amateur bands.

The best type of mixer for use in these receivers is the *balanced mixer*, and some manufacturers produce ready-made balanced mixer modules incorporating the diodes and necessary transformer. In the examples shown in Figures 6.2a and b, the two-diode mixer can be balanced by adjusting a preset resistor. This balancing is used to ensure that strong signals near the one of interest do not break through into

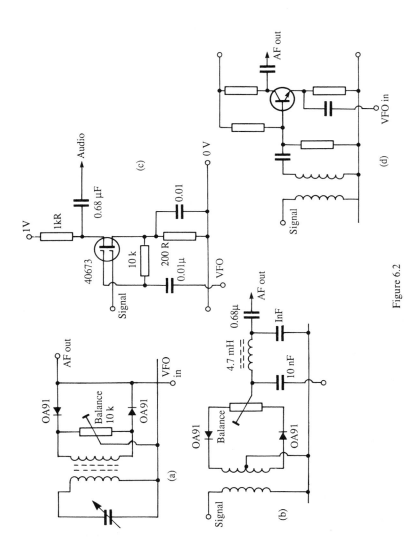

Figure 6.2

the detector and audio stages of the receiver and so produce an un-tunable signal. DC receivers are particularly prone to this for two reasons:

1 the selectivity of a DC receiver is purely that offered by the AF filter. The front end tuning is likely to be quite broad, and so many potentially quite strong signals will get through to the detector stage

2 if the detector is not properly balanced, then detection of signals will occur in the same way that a crystal set detects signals. Even tiny amounts of imbalance can lead to considerable output signals from interfering stations due to the high level of audio gain present in DC receivers.

The RF front end

This can be just a simple tuned circuit feeding directly into the product detector, or it can incorporate some form of RF amplifier (Figure 6.3). DC receivers rarely have a large tuning span, so it is possible to have a fixed frequency tuned circuit, centered on the middle of the band of interest. If a variable capacitor is used at this stage of the circuit, it is often used as a bandset control. Some designs have appeared in magazines covering, say, both the 160 and 80 m amateur bands, with a wide band tuned circuit such that 160 m signals were tuned in with the oscillator with the bandset control at one end of its range and 80 m at the other end of the range, with switching on the oscillator to vary the range of frequencies covered. The bandwidth required in this input RF stage depends upon the amateur bands that the receiver is intended for use on. For example, a set designed for use on the 40 m amateur band might only need a bandwidth of about 100 kHz, centered around 7050 kHz. This would allow the input stage to limit the number of strong broadcast stations getting to the mixer. Finally, although it is possible, it is not a good idea to dispense with the input stage all together and just connect the aerial to the mixer: this would almost certainly result in breakthrough!

The oscillator stage

The RF oscillator must produce a stable signal at a reasonable output level. This requires that it is built as sturdily as possible. Some typical oscillator arrangements are shown in Figure 6.4a. The oscillator is totally responsible for receiver stability: if the oscillator wanders in

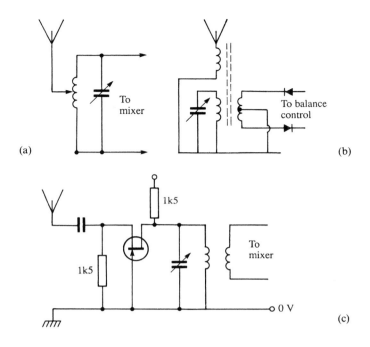

Figure 6.3

frequency then so will the signals received. For most listening use, it is short term accuracy that is most important; the oscillator may well drift in frequency by a few kHz over a *long* period of time but as you will probably be listening to a station for no more than a couple of minutes at a time, drift will be of little significance. However, if drift is, say, 50 or 60 Hz each *second* it will make listening to SSB transmissions difficult, to say the least. The tuning range of oscillators used in DC receivers is usually quite small, spanning only the specific frequencies required. A DC receiver tuning the 80 m amateur band would thus cover the frequencies 3.5 MHz to 3.85 MHz or so.

The buffer stage (typical circuits are shown in Figure 6.4b) is quite useful, in two respects:

1 it can be used to boost up the oscillator signal

2 It produces a degree of isolation between the oscillator and the input tuned circuits, and so reduces the effects of pulling of the oscillator

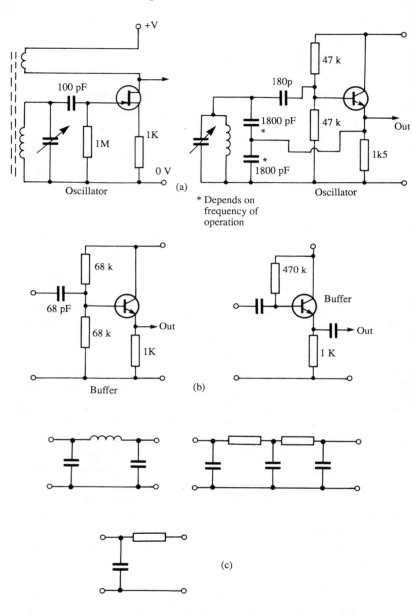

Figure 6.4

frequency, either when the input stage is tuned or, in extreme cases, when the aerial moves in the wind!

The oscillator used should be 'clean', and not produce harmonic signals. Harmonics often arise when we try to get too much output from a single transistor circuit. It is a much better proposition to use a buffer stage to amplify the oscillator output rather than overdrive a single stage oscillator. In addition, a buffer stage gives us a useful extra if we are wanting an accurate read out of the frequency to which the receiver is tuned; the output from the buffer can be used to drive the input of a frequency meter, again with no ill effects on the oscillator.

The AF filter

The AF filter defines the selectivity of a DC receiver, and is effectively a low pass filter. These were described in Chapter 1, and the cut off frequency required can be calculated as was shown. For CW reception, a cut off frequency of 1 kHz or even less would be adequate, whereas a cut off of around 3 kHz is required for SSB resolution.

Alternatively, a bandpass filter (Chapter 10) might be considered for CW reception, or even a circuit based on a PLL chip, like the CW terminal unit shown in Chapter 10.

It is important that this filter gets rid of all the RF signals that might be around rather than passing them through to the audio amplifier, as this could cause serious instability problems. A number of typical AF filters are shown in Figure 6.4c.

The AF amplifier

The gain of a DC receiver is defined overwhelmingly by the audio amplifier stage. For this reason, a high gain amplifier is required. This can be provided by transistors or integrated circuit packages.

Using the receiver

When setting up a DC receiver, the first thing to do is to adjust the balance control, if present, to minimise breakthrough from other stations. Additional precautions to take include using attenuators at the aerial (Chapter 10) or having a looser coupling between aerial, tuned circuit and mixer to minimise signal transfer.

Resolving SSB and CW signals

CW signals are easy to resolve on a DC receiver. The local oscillator is tuned to a frequency a little above or below that of the desired signal. It does not matter which side of the signal we tune the oscillator; just tune for the minimum noise and interference. The oscillator will then beat with the CW signals, in sympathy with the morse code characters being sent thus producing an audio tone as a beat note. The pitch of the tone can be adjusted to suit your ear, a 'zero beat' indicating the exact frequency on which the station is transmitting.

Resolving SSB transmissions is not such an easy job, as we have to take note of whether the signal involved is an LSB or USB signal.

If you are resolving LSB signals then the oscillator should be tuned so that the signal it generates is slightly *above* the signal that you are attempting to resolve. A few seconds thought will indicate why this is so; the LSB signal is transmitted without upper sideband or carrier, the latter being immediately above the lower sideband in frequency. The oscillator signal is effectively replacing the carrier signal, and fine adjustment of the oscillator frequency will allow the pitch of the voice to be adjusted so that it sounds less like Donald Duck and more like a human being!

On the other hand, when resolving USB signals, the oscillator is tuned so as to be slightly *below* the desired signal in frequency. The oscillator is replacing the carrier wave that was originally slightly below the upper sideband.

Tuning the oscillator to the wrong side of a signal will result in totally unintelligible speech, as the low pitched parts of the voice signal will be reproduced as relatively high pitched sounds and vice versa. This 'mirror image' of speech is easily recognised as being this, because no matter how you tune the signal you will be unable to resolve it in to intelligible speech. Thus, on SSB signals, we cannot tune to the side of the signal that has the lowest amount of noise or interference; all we can do is tune to the correct side of the signal frequency and do our best!

In practical terms, this means that when tuning through amateur bands on a DC receiver we should start at the HF ends of the bands on which LSB is used as the predominant SSB mode and tune downwards in frequency, and start at the lower ends of the bands where USB is the predominant mode and tune upwards in frequency. This will allow us to tune in such a way that a voice signal will be resolved first, rather than having to tune through the mirror image signal first. LSB tends to be used on the bands below 10 MHz, and USB above 10 MHz.

You can thus see that for any SSB or CW signal, the receiver will have two places on the dial where the signal can be heard, one above and one below the actual signal frequency. This effect is known as *audio imaging*, and in simple designs I am afraid we are stuck with it, although design techniques do exist to get rid of one image. With SSB signals, the image is easy to spot; that is the signal that resolves as total gobbledegook. However, it is no real problem – just do not log the same CW signal twice, once on each side of the signal frequency!

Resolving AM signals

AM signals can be resolved with DC receivers, but I would not suggest you build one for broadcast band listening! When tuning an AM signal, a heterodyne whistle will be heard as you tune through the sidebands of the signal; this is the beat note caused by the oscillator frequency and the carrier signal beating with each other. As you reach the carrier frequency of the signal, you will hear the note decrease in pitch until it is a zero beat, where you will probably perceive a growl caused by phase differences between the oscillator and the carrier. In home-made sets, you may also find some growling and wow on signals due to oscillator drift! Music does not always come out of DC receivers in a recognisable state; a voice may sound perfectly alright even when the oscillator tuning is not quite spot on, but music is much more frequency dependant, and will show up any discrepancies between the oscillator tuning and the carrier signal.

Some practical ideas

Figure 6.5 shows two experimental circuits that you might like to try setting up, although I have given no component layout diagram. The only thing to watch is construction of the oscillator circuit. This should be as rigid as possible, and to reduce hand capacity effects you should use the techniques described in Chapter 5. To reduce any risk of interference to other receivers working on the band concerned in your area, you might like to build the receiver in a metal box. You might like to alter these designs to work on other frequencies by adjusting the coils used. Be wary, however, that at higher frequencies the oscillator frequency may not be stable enough to give good results. The receivers are used in the way described above.

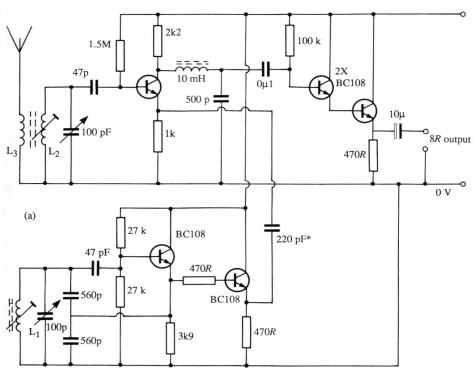

(a)

* Experiment for best results
L_1 – oscillator coil – 30 turns on 1/4 in diameter former with ferrite slug for tuning
L_2 – tuning coil as L_1
L_3 – aerial coil – 15 turns over 'earthy' end of L_2
(tunes 80 M band, roughly. Change turns to change frequency.
The two 560 pF capacitors will need to be reduced for higher frequencies.)

Figure 6.5(a)

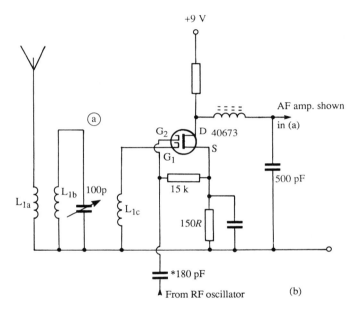

+9 V

(a)

AF amp. shown
in (a)

G_2 D 40673

G_1 S

L_{1b} 100p

L_{1a}

L_{1c}

15 k

150R

500 pF

*180 pF

From RF oscillator   (b)

* Experiment for best results
L1a, L1b as L3, L2 in (a)
L1c wound over 'aerial' end of L1b – 15 turns.
Alternatively connect G1 to point A directly.

Figure 6.5(b)

SEVEN

Superheterodyne receivers

Despite the results that can be obtained with simple regenerative or direct conversion receivers, the *superheterodyne* receiver – *superhet* for short – is the standard receiver against which other types of design are measured.

Providing high gain and good selectivity over a wide frequency range is not easy; requiring careful adjustment and design if instability is to be prevented. We saw this ourselves in the way in which the regeneration control has to be constantly adjusted to maintain optimum selectivity and sensitivity in a regenerative receiver. However, getting good selectivity and high gain at one particular frequency is relatively straightforward. So, if we could convert *all* incoming signals to *one* frequency, and provide all the receiver's gain and selectivity at this frequency, we could have a highly stable, sensitive and selective receiver. This is the superhet.

The fixed frequency, called the *intermediate frequency* (IF), for historical reasons, can be higher or lower than the signals being received and is generated by mixing the incoming radio signal with a signal from a circuit called a *local oscillator*, which is simply a tunable RF oscillator. This mixing process produces sum and difference signals, and the difference between the two signals is used as the IF and is amplified by a narrow bandwidth tuned amplifier called the *IF amplifier*, or *IF strip*, of the receiver. The signal leaving the IF strip can be up to 1000 times greater than that entering it, and it provides the majority of gain in a superhet receiver. The IF signal is then demodulated to resolve the audio that the signal was carrying, and with suitable detector circuits a superhet can resolve AM, CW, SSB and even NBFM.

Figure 7.1 shows the block diagram of a typical *single conversion* superhet receiver, named because the input signals are converted just

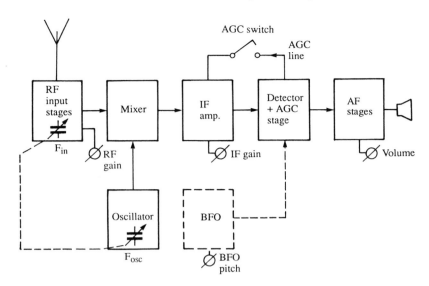

Figure 7.1

once to another frequency. The oscillator tuning control and that of the RF input circuits are mechanically linked together – *ganged* – so that the difference between the oscillator frequency and the frequency to which the input tuned circuits are tuned is always equal to the IF of the receiver. This ensures that the mixer, sometimes referred to as the *frequency changer*, always produces the IF as the difference frequency. If this were not to happen, then at some frequencies the IF signal produced might be outside the pass band of the IF strip, and so the receiver would be extremely insensitive at these frequencies. The oscillator usually runs at a frequency above the tuned signals, and the ability of the receiver tuning circuits to maintain the IF between oscillator tuning and input tuning is called the *tracking* of the receiver. This is rarely perfect, but the differences in sensitivity at different parts of the frequency coverage due to poor tracking would not be noticed unless it is really bad! Figure 7.2 shows a couple of oscillator/mixer combinations, one in which separate active devices are used for mixer and oscillator and the second in which both jobs are done by the same transistor, a common course of action in cheaper receivers.

The IF strip consists of one or more tuned amplifiers, with a response that peaks at the IF in use. The bandwidth of the IF strip

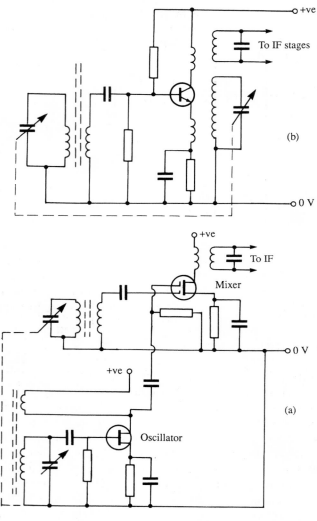

Figure 7.2

defines the bandwidth of the receiver and so needs to be chosen with the signals of interest in mind. A MW portable designed for entertainment might have a fairly wide bandwidth of 6 kHz or more, centred on the IF, so as to not lose quality on transmitted music. A communications receiver usually has switchable bandwidths, often in the form of filters before or after the IF stage but before the detector. The IF bandwidth can then be fairly wide, and enhanced selectivity provided by the filters. Typical bandwidths for different modes of operation could be:

entertainment quality AM	9 kHz
communications quality AM	6 kHz
SSB	3 kHz
CW	800 Hz

The gain of the IF strip can be controlled in two ways. The first is manual, where a receiver control allows the gain of the IF strip to be adjusted. The second is automatic, via a system called automatic gain control (AGC). Here, a portion of the detected signal is sampled and used to control the gain of the IF strip. If a very strong signal is received, the AGC will act to reduce the IF gain, and vice versa. The result of this is to maintain receiver output level at a constant level for a variety of different input signal strengths. In some receivers, it is possible to disable the AGC, and this is often done for resolving SSB and CW signals. The voltage on the AGC line gives us an idea of the signal strength at a given moment, and so is often monitored to give a meter reading of received signals strength (the S-meter).

The output signal from the IF strip is then demodulated. The most common detector found in simple sets is a diode demodulator (Figure 7.3a), very similar to that found in a crystal set. This will obviously resolve AM signals, and with an additional circuit, the *beat frequency oscillator* (BFO), can resolve SSB and CW signals as well.

The BFO

This is a simple, tunable RF oscillator operating over a range of frequencies within a couple of kilohertz of the receiver IF. The output from this circuit is introduced to either the last IF stage or the input to the detector stage, and allows CW and SSB signals to be resolved.

With CW, the BFO signal causes a beat note to be generated in the presence of the carrier signal. The pitch of the note depends upon the difference in frequency between the BFO and the IF, and so in receivers with a continuously adjustable BFO (usually giving a range around the IF frequency of plus or minus 3 kHz or so), the pitch can be adjusted *and* the user can decide whether to use the BFO on the low side of the IF or the high side; either side will work.

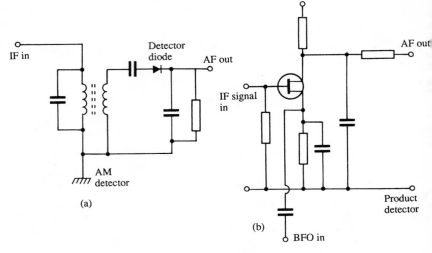

Figure 7.3

With SSB signals, the BFO signal effectively replaces the carrier wave removed at transmission. To demodulate LSB signals, the BFO should be adjusted to be on the high side of the IF, and for USB signal the BFO frequency should be slightly below the IF. Complete details of tuning in SSB signals on superhets are found in Chapter 11.

A more efficient detector for CW/SSB signals is a product detector (Figure 7.3b), and a block diagram of a combined AM/SSB/CW system is shown in Figure 7.4.

Resolving NBFM signals is possible with an AM detector using a technique called *slope detection*. This will work with any type of receiver capable of resolving AM and is discussed in Chapter 11.

Alternatively, special NBFM detectors can be built into the receiver. A relatively wide bandwidth, often around 12 kHz, is needed for good NBFM reception. Figure 7.4 shows some typical detector circuits for the different transmission modes. After detection, the audio stages of a receiver may include noise limiters and possibly notch filters, as well as an audio amplifier to bring the signals up to loudspeaker strength.

Choice of IF

This is a very important choice in a superhet receiver. Popular IFs for domestic MW/LW receivers are between 455 and 470 kHz, 465 kHz

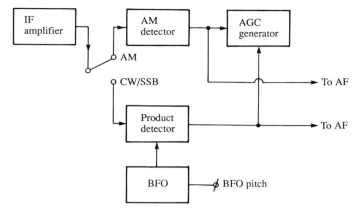

Figure 7.4

being quite popular. Other receivers, designed for shortwave reception may have IFs of around 1.6 MHz. The IF should be such that there are no strong stations operating on or near the IF frequency. These signals could get in to the IF strip, be demodulated by the detector and appear as untuneable interference on all stations, an effect called *IF break-through*. If this does occur, it can be prevented by inserting a tuned circuit at the IF frequency of the receiver in the aerial input of the receiver. Such a circuit is called an *IF trap*.

A second consideration is that IFs at low frequencies are easier to design and build than those at higher frequencies, as are the oscillator circuits needed to produce the IF. However, low IF frequencies, below about 1 MHz, can suffer from *image reception* (see later). In addition, the oscillator should not produce harmonics on any of the frequency bands that the receiver is designed to cover. This again limits the choice of IF frequency.

Problems with superhets

Image reception

I once read a comment by *Cathode Ray*, one time columnist of the magazine *Wireless World*, who said something to the effect that 'A superhet receiver picks up all stations, some of them more than once!' He was referring to the big disadvantage of superhet receivers – *image reception*, where signals are received that are not really there!

It is best explained by example. Imagine a receiver with a 470 kHz IF tuned to a station on 14300 kHz. The oscillator, as is commonly the case in many superhets, runs at a higher frequency than the desired signal, and so will be found on 14770 kHz (14770 − 14300 = 470 kHz IF). However, a few minutes thought will indicate that a strong signal 470 kHz *above* the oscillator frequency would *also* give an IF of 470 kHz to be processed by the receiver, which does not mind whether the IF signal is arrived at from the desired signal on 14300 kHz or the *image* signal on 14770 + 470 = 15240 kHz. This image frequency is slap bang in the middle of the 19 metre broadcast band, and so strong stations are not going to be thin on the ground! For this reason, good input tuned circuits are required to allow the desired frequency through to the mixer but to prevent the image frequency getting through. With low IFs and simple input tuning, the image may easily get through, especially on the higher frequencies. There are two solutions; increase the Q of the input circuits, hence limiting the bandwidth, or increase the IF. Images occur at $f_d + 2$ IF, where f_d is the frequency of the desired signal, and so increasing the IF will increase the frequency separation between desired signal and image.

Birdies

A *birdy* (called this because it often 'tweets' when you tune it!) is a tunable carrier wave generated by the receiver circuits themselves, often coming from the local oscillator. In bad cases, birdies can give rise to image frequency problems, as explained above. Cures for birdies include:

1 better suppression of harmonic output from the local oscillator, if this is the source

2 screening of any parts of the receiver generating RF signals, such as oscillators used for second or third IF generation (see later), or digital frequency meters.

One cause of oscillator harmonics can be strong signals overloading the mixer and driving it in to non-linearity. This will produce harmonics of the oscillator *and* of any mixer products; a veritable forest of spurious signals can soon spring up in this way! A simple cure is to use an attenuator to reduce the strength of signals reaching the mixer, especially on the 49 and 41 metre broadcast bands in Europe in the evening. This is an example of poor strong-signal handling, and modern semiconductor-based mixers are often poor in this respect.

Cross modulation

Strong signals causing the mixer to become non-linear can also cause the modulation of strong, undesired, signals to become imposed upon that of a weaker station of interest, even when the two signals are on totally different frequencies. This makes it impossible to separate the stations by tuning, and the only cure is to reduce the mixer overloading by reducing the strength of incoming signals.

Intermodulation

Another source of lots of spurious signals! Two very strong signals can mix themselves together, producing images over several hundred kilohertz. For example, a strong signal on 6100 kHz and one on 6180 kHz might drive the mixer into non-linearity and produce signals every 80 kHz over the neighbouring frequencies. Maybe Radio Moscow has not got all those broadcasts at all . . .

Blocking

Here, strong signals can cause a reduction in gain of the receiver (*desensitisation*) or total deafness on a particular portion of a frequency band (*blocking*).

Some cures for all these ailments include the following:

1 use of attenuators to reduce signal strength. The spurious signals usually disappear before the real signals do, and the resultant silence can be heaven!

2 an aerial tuning unit or a preselector (see Chapter 10) can improve rejection of image frequency signals

3 avoid using high gain aerial amplifiers or active antennas unless you can put some attenuation in between the amplifier and receiver front end. This will allow you to attenuate signals when the system is used in bands with very strong signals.

Double conversion superhets

Although a high IF provides immunity from image frequency problems, it is easier to produce high gain, selective amplifiers at lower

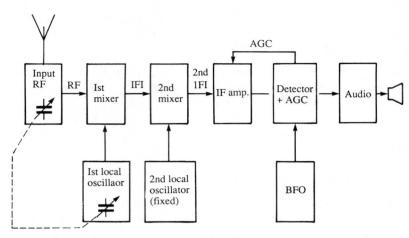

Figure 7.5

frequencies. So, the *double conversion superhet* was born, where a first, relatively high IF is used to reduce image reception problems and a second IF is used to provide the gain and selectivity. Little, if any, amplification is provided at the high IF (Figure 7.5).

BFO injection occurs at the lower IF, which is often 465 kHz. The first IF can be anywhere between 1.6 MHz and 40 or 50 MHz. Some receivers are single conversion on some frequency bands, say MW and LW, but double conversion on the short wave bands. The more frequency changes involved in a receiver, the greater the potential problems with spurious signals such as birdies, and care needs to be taken with design of such receivers.

Triple conversion receivers include a further oscillator/frequency changer combination and the third IF is often as low as 80 or 90 kHz.

The Wadley loop system

One disadvantage of the highly selective, narrow bandwidth tuning used in IF strips is that if the oscillator used to produce the IF signal drifts a little in frequency as the set warms up with use, or the operating environment of the receiver changes temperature, then it is quite possible for the IF to fall outside the passband of the IF amplifier, no matter how good tracking is. This drift gives rise to frequent retuning to keep the desired signal in the middle of the IF passband.

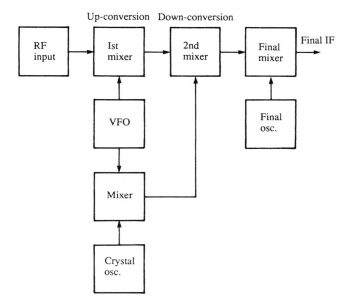

Figure 7.6

The *Wadley loop drift cancellation system* (Figure 7.6) has been employed in several receivers, notably the Yaesu FRG7 and the Lowe SRX30, to minimise drift. It is a multiple conversion superhet, with the first IF considerably *higher* than the described signals. The incoming signals are thus up-converted to the first IF, which is often in the 40 to 70 MHz frequency range. The clever bit is that the same oscillator used to produce the first IF is also used, via a further mixing process involving a highly stable crystal oscillator, to *down-convert* the IF to a second IF, often of several megahertz. A third conversion can take the IF down to a more workable 1.6 MHz or 465 kHz. By using the same VFO to provide up and down conversion in this way, drift is cancelled out. For example, any upwards drift in frequency of the first oscillator will cause an upward drift in the first IF signal generated. However, this drift will cause a corresponding *downwards* frequency change for the down conversion process, and the two drifts will cancel out.

Digital techniques

Recent developments in the field of digital electronics have made their impact on receiver design, culminating in the latest receivers which can be controlled by a home computer. Simpler applications of digital electronics include the use of digital frequency meters and frequency synthesisers.

1 Digital frequency meters

The output of the local oscillator can be linked to the input of a special integrated circuit that measures the frequency of the oscillator. This, of course, does not give a true measure of the frequency of the incoming signal; it would differ from it by the IF. However, these chips are capable of being programmed with common IF frequencies and they automatically subtract the IF from the oscillator frequency. They can be very accurate, with resolutions often down to 100 Hz or even 10 Hz in the more expensive receivers. A common resolution on most sets is 1 kHz.

Frequency meters, being digital circuits, can generate an awful lot of interference from their circuits due to the presence of square wave pulse trains that drive the various parts of the frequency meter. In addition the clock circuit, which might be running anywhere between 100 kHz and a few megahertz, will generate harmonics all the way across the frequency spectrum. To get around this, frequency meters need proper design and construction, with as much of the circuit shielded from the RF input circuits of the receiver as possible – even then the odd spurious response may be noted. Where these are depends upon the design of the receiver, and prominent spurious signals should be listed in a manufacturer's information for the receiver. Some frequency meters are made switchable, so that they are only bought in to play when a measurement of frequency is required. The process often simultaneously mutes the receiver audio, so that any interference caused is not heard by the user!

2 Frequency synthesis

The second main application of digital technology in receiver design is a technique called *frequency synthesis*, where the oscillator used to produce the first IF is no longer a traditional LC or crystal circuit but is a highly stable system which allows frequencies to be tuned in steps of 10 or 100 Hz. The size of these steps is called the resolution of the receiver, and many synthesised receivers have a means of varying the step size for faster tuning. For example, a set may have 10 Hz step size for fine tuning a station, but 1 kHz step size for scanning the bands. A high step size can make the tuning of SSB a little difficult, as it is not possible to tune between the minimum step size on some receivers. The obvious solution is to have a small minimum step size, often 10 Hz in more expensive receivers, or to incorporate some form of continuous fine tuning over a few kilohertz around the tuned frequency. Frequency readout is invariably in the form of a digital display.

Apart from the stepped nature of the tuning, frequency synthesisers can give rise to other problems:

1 *Glitches.* Tuning certain frequencies may give rise to 'pinging' noises. This is produced by the receiver. Until I realised this, I had great fun trying to tune a few of these in!

2 *Synthesiser noise.* Frequency synthesisers produce more noise in the oscillator signal than do traditional oscillator designs. Some of this noise may be of a high enough level to cause a generally higher background noise level in the receiver.

3 *Jitter.* Synthesisers can 'flip' between adjacent frequencies, causing a jitter in the tuned frequency by the step size. This will detune the incoming signal, causing random fluctuations in signal strength, especially on narrow band transmission modes such as RTTY or CW.

More information on choosing and using superhet receivers is in Chapter 11.

EIGHT

Converters

A superheterodyne receiver is not really a suitable constructional project unless you have got adequate test gear for its alignment. However, the principle involved, that of converting incoming signals from one frequency to another can be used to allow a domestic MW receiver to resolve signals on the HF bands without affecting its MW performance. An electronic circuit called a *converter* is used; this works like the front end of a superhet, converting incoming short wave signals into a frequency that can be picked up on a MW receiver standing next to the converter. The MW receiver then provides IF amplification and detection. In fact, we have got a very simple double superhet design (Figure 8.1).

Two signals, one from the aerial tuned circuit and one from the oscillator are mixed to provide the IF. If FI is the input frequency from the aerial and FO is the oscillator frequency, the mixing process gives: FI + FO, and; FI − FO (or FO − FI, depending upon whether the oscillator is higher or lower than the input signal frequency). Thus, either the sum or difference signal can be used as an IF and when we are using a MW receiver as the IF strip, it is usual to use the difference signal so that the oscillator runs at a higher frequency than the frequencies that we are interested in receiving. This avoids any problems with harmonics of the oscillator producing birdies (see Chapter 7) in the receiver.

There are two main approaches to converter design, and they differ in whether the tuning of different stations is done by adjusting controls on the receiver or the converter.

In the first case, the receiver acts essentially as a tuned IF. The converter has a fixed frequency oscillator, and its input tuned circuit and IF tuning have quite wide passbands (Figure 8.2). A receiver, tuning the normal MW band of 500 kHz to 1.6 MHz would be able to

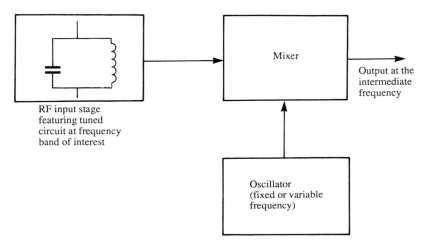

Figure 8.1

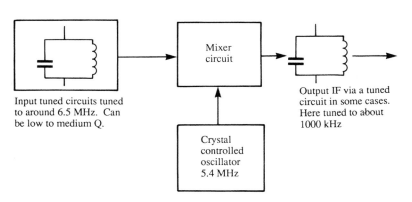

Figure 8.2

tune over a 1.1 MHz portion of the short wave band. In the example shown, the receiver is able to tune signals in the range 5.9 to 7 MHz, with the oscillator running *below* the desired input frequency. If we were to run the oscillator *above* the desired frequency when using the tuned IF technique, we would get a rather interesting problem called *frequency inversion*; an oscillator running at 7.5 MHz would result in a tuning position at 500 kHz on the MW set bringing in signals on 7 MHz, whilst a tuning position at 1.6 MHz would bring in signals on

5.9 MHz. There is nothing wrong with this, it is just a little confusing until you get used to it! The tuned circuits should be designed to have a bandwidth of about 1 MHz, centred on 6.45 MHz for the input circuit and about 1050 kHz for the IF output tuned circuit.

Other IF frequencies may be used, and the technique is often employed to allow a short wave receiver tuning the range 28 to 30 MHz to tune signals in the VHF part of the frequency spectrum. A VHF converter changes the VHF signals into signals in the range 28 to 30 MHz. Another popular range for a tuned IF is 3 to 4 MHz. The advantages of this configuration are as follows:

1 all the tuned circuits in the converter are fixed, and the oscillator can be crystal controlled. This simplifies converter construction

2 the tuning dial of the receiver can be used, and knowing the frequency to which we are tuned on the RX dial, and the oscillator frequency, we can get an accurate frequency measurement.

On the other hand, the disadvantages are:

1 precautions must be taken to eliminate IF breakthrough. For example, when tuning a MW receiver hooked up to a converter we might easily receive strong MW broadcast stations as well as the desired short wave stations

2 the tuning range is limited to that of the receiver being used as the tuned IF. Thus a MW receiver can only cover the spectrum in 1.1 MHz chunks.

Because of the possibility of IF breakthrough, converters in this configuration must be linked to the receiver being used as the tuned IF in such a way as to minimise the receiver's pickup of any signals other than those originating from the converter. This is not too difficult if the receiver has an aerial socket; screened cable is simply used to make the connection. However, with a typical MW receiver with its built-in ferrite rod aerial (Chapter 10) it is just about impossible. For receivers with aerial sockets, we need to consider the IF frequency range used. European listeners might be unwise to use a 6 to 7 MHz IF, due to the number of powerful broadcasters in that range.

In the second type of converter, shown in Figure 8.3, tuning is done on the converter, and the receiver used is tuned to a fixed IF output from the converter. In effect, the converter is the front end of a conventional superheterodyne receiver! Tuning of oscillator and aerial tuning

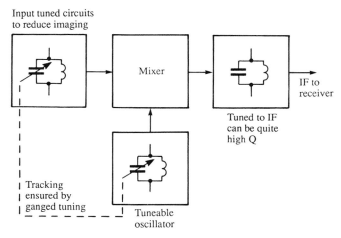

Input tuned circuits
to reduce imaging

Mixer

IF to
receiver

Tuned to IF
can be quite
high Q

Tracking
ensured by
ganged tuning

Tuneable
oscillator

Figure 8.3

circuits should, ideally, be ganged to ensure good tracking across the range of frequencies covered (Chapter 7) but this would complicate matters and, for our purposes, is not strictly necessary, as we will soon see.

The IF output of such a converter is chosen to be a frequency normally devoid of strong signals. For converters designed for MW receivers, 1.6 MHz is a common choice. In addition, a high IF reduces the problems caused by image reception, which is just as much a problem with converters as it is with superheterodyne receivers. Because we can choose an IF ourselves, IF breakthrough is no longer a great problem – we simply pick a quiet IF – and so it becomes feasible to use converters with any MW receiver, even those with a ferrite rod aerial.

With this type of converter, tuning is carried out by adjusting the frequency of the converter oscillator to tune in a signal with the input tuned circuit being further adjusted to peak up the volume. In technical terms, the input tuned circuit is a bandset control and the oscillator tuning actually determines the exact frequency that is converted to the IF. A tuning range of several megahertz is thus easily achieved. However, good mechanical mounting is required for the oscillator tuning control, similar to that needed for the regenerative receiver. In addition, a slow motion drive and a means of suppressing hand capacity effects is also desirable.

Once the fixed/variable IF decision is made, the next step is to decide

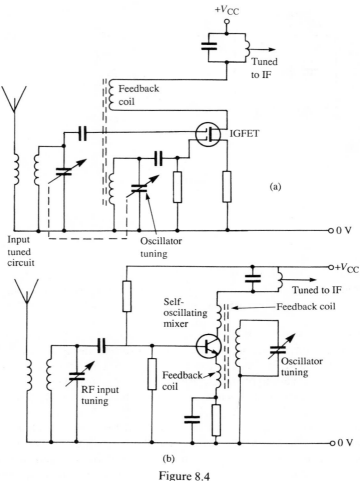

Figure 8.4

whether to go for a *self-oscillating mixer* or separate oscillator and mixer circuits. In the former, the job of oscillator and mixer is carried out by one active device and thus significantly simplifies circuitry. In the latter case, separate active devices are employed, and this can give better results at the cost of the circuit being a little more complex. The self-oscillating mixer design is easier to build, though, and will still give reasonable service. As far as active devices are concerned, FETs or bipolar transistors are used as both oscillators and mixers. IGFETs

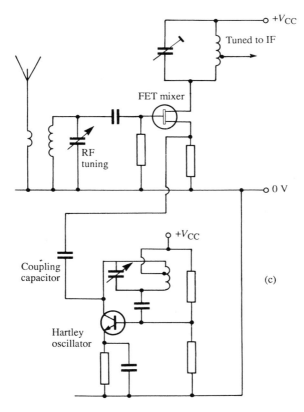

Figure 8.4 (cont.)

(see Chapter 1) are quite popular as mixers – some have two input electrodes and they are more resistant than bipolar devices to overloading problems. Figure 8.4 shows a few possible converter arrangements; the Reinartz arrangement in Figure 8.4b is quite popular as the mixer stage of cheap MW portables due to its relative simplicity. In that particular application, though, oscillator and input tuning controls are ganged.

Coupling of the IF of these converters to the receiver can be direct to the aerial socket of the receiver or by inductive coupling between the output tuned circuit of the converter and the ferrite rod aerial of the receiver.

Whatever converter design is used, an RF pre-amplifier may be a useful add-on, between aerial and mixer; not so much for the gain provided but for the isolation between mixer/oscillator and aerial. This will reduce the amount of RF at the oscillator frequency that finds its way to the aerial and is radiated as interference. If a pre-amplifier stage is not used, then the coupling between aerial and mixer should be fairly loose. See Chapter 5 for hints on how to adjust aerial coupling.

The type of signals that can be demodulated by a converter/receiver combination depend upon the receiver in use, which does not have to be a superhet. Indeed, you could use a converter with a fixed-tuned regenerative receiver, and use control of regeneration to resolve AM, CW and SSB signals. If a MW superheterodyne is used, then a beat frequency oscillator is required to resolve CW or SSB signals received.

Problems

Because we are effectively building the front end of a superhet set when we build a converter, the problems associated with converters are very similar to those suffered by superhets.

Image reception

We have already seen how an image signal can be caused. As a worked example, imagine a converter receiving a signal on 6 MHz with an oscillator running at 7.6 MHz thus giving an IF of 1.6 MHz. A signal of 9.2 MHz will also give a 1.6 MHz IF, and so stations around the 31 metre band might pop up whilst tuning the 49 metre band. We can peak up desired signals and reduce the level of image signals by tuning the input bandset tuned circuits. It would, of course, be possible to peak up the image signal if the bandset capacitor were incorrectly set! This is one reason why frequencies around 1.6 MHz are used as IFs in preference to lower ones; the image frequency is further away from the frequency of interest – twice the IF away, in fact – and so the simple input tuned circuits are adequate to select easily between the two signals.

Image reception can also be caused by harmonics from the oscillator beating with other signals; this will usually give rise to whistles when the converter is tuned. The cure is to reduce the number of harmonics generated by the oscillator to a minimum, usually by biasing the oscillator to be as linear as possible.

Overloading

A further difficulty can be overloading. With converters, two types of overloading can be experienced:

1 *converter overload.* Here the mixer stage of the converter is over-loaded by strong signals, and problems of untunable signals, etc. will arise as they did with the superheterodyne receiver

2 *receiver overload.* Here the input to the receiver from the converter is so strong that it overloads the receiver mixer, giving similar effects.

The former problem is cured by reducing signal input by using attenuators or an aerial tuning unit. The second requires the coupling between receiver and converter to be reduced, either by putting a capacitor in the cable linking the IF output of a converter to the aerial input of the receiver or by changing the position of the converter with respect to the receiver if inductive coupling between the converter output and receiver ferrite rod aerial is used.

A simple converter

The circuit diagram in Figure 8.5 is of a simple converter circuit that will allow a large part of the short wave spectrum to be received on a conventional MW receiver tuned to around 1.6 MHz. The converter uses a self-oscillating mixer (TR_2 and associated components) and an RF input stage formed by TR_1 which:

1 isolates the aerial from the oscillator and so reduces any chance of signals from the oscillator reaching the aerial
2 prevents the aerial from loading the oscillator too heavily and so prevents the oscillator from working correctly.

Input tuning is done by L_1/VC_1, and oscillator tuning by VC_2/L_2. The latter tuned circuit should always cover a slightly greater frequency range than the input tuned circuit so that the 1.6 MHz difference frequency is available across the whole oscillator tuning range, thus allowing VC_1 to peak up signals at any setting of VC_2. This should be remembered if you try rewinding the coils to cover different frequency ranges. The oscillator runs at a higher frequency than the input signal.

The oscillator is a fairly well behaved circuit, and trimming capacitor TC_1 is present to allow you to 'tweak' the oscillator for best performance with different frequency ranges. The circuit is tolerant of

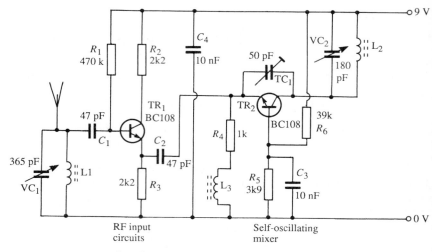

Figure 8.5

L_1 – 8 turns on 3 in ferrite rod
L_2 – 6 turns on 3 in ferrite rod
L_3 – 60 turns on 6 in ferrite rod

different transistor types; although BC108s are specified, other general-purpose or RF NPN transistors should also work. I tried the circuit with 2N2222 and ZTX300 transistors, as well as a couple of dubious looking transistors rescued from a defunct Japanese tranny! All worked well. The coupling coil, L_3, is simply a MW tuning coil like that used in the crystal set of Chapter 4. Alternatively, 60 turns on a 6 in ferrite rod is quite adequate. The coil is connected as part of the emitter load of TR_2 and so has currents at the IF and oscillator frequency flowing through it. The receiver tuning will, however, separate these signals.

Figure 8.6 shows a component layout for the circuit. Both tuning controls should be mounted on an insulated panel some distance behind the front panel of the receiver. This is because the front panel and chassis should be connected to 0 V for screening purposes. Shafts of the two tuning controls should be extended with a nylon or plastic rod, or wooden dowel. A slow motion drive (8:1 in the prototype) is essential, as tuning is very sharp indeed. The extension of the two controls in this way reduces hand capacity effects. Feel free to try other methods of mounting these controls but do remember that *neither* set

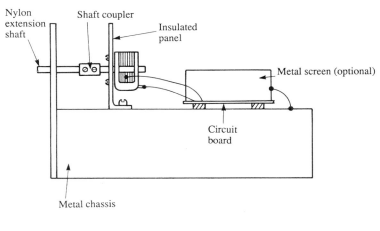

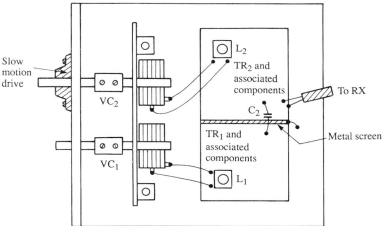

Figure 8.6

of vanes of VC_2 is connected to 0 V and so this component needs to be insulated from the front panel in some way. The only other thing to note is the positioning of coils $L_{1,2}$ and $_3$. L_1 and $_2$ should be mounted at right angles to each other (to reduce inductive coupling) and as far apart as possible on the chassis. L_3 should be connected to the Veroboard via a length of co-axial cable so that it can be positioned next to the receiver ferrite rod aerial. The braid of the co-ax should go to 0 V, but this is not vital. Any 9 V battery will power the circuit; I used a PP7.

Testing and setting up

Position L_3 as close to the ferrite rod aerial of the receiver as possible, and tune the receiver to a spot around 1600 kHz that is devoid of signals. It helps to do this in the evening, when any more distant Continental stations that may interfere will be audible. Now connect up the aerial to the converter and apply power. TC_1 should be adjusted to about $\frac{1}{4}$ full capacity, using an insulated trimming tool. Now adjust VC_2 tuning the oscillator until a station is heard: VC_1 can then be adjusted to peak up the volume. It is likely that if a station is tuned in with VC_2 virtually closed, the setting on VC_1 for maximum volume will also be almost closed. There will, of course, be a difference in the degree of meshing of the tuning controls but it should not be too great. Now tune to a signal with the oscillator tuning control VC_2 almost fully meshed. If nothing is heard, increase the capacity of TC_1 by closing it slightly until a station, or an increase in noise, *can* be tuned. Tune across the band, and if you detect any whistles or squeaks on signals, open TC_1 very slightly. You may need to repeat the whole procedure a few times until a compromise setting of TC_1 is established. Once stations can be tuned across the whole range of VC_2, however, TC_1 can be left alone unless you change coils, when it may need readjustment.

Now tune in a station and adjust the position of L_3 for maximum volume in the receiver.

In the prototype receiver, with the coils as described, frequency coverage was from around 4 MHz to 13 MHz and reception of signals from all over the world was experienced, including Radio Australia on the 31 metre band.

In use, the usual method of working is as follows:

1 if you are looking for signals in the LF end of the band, adjust VC_1 so that it is about $\frac{3}{4}$ meshed; for HF, adjust until it is only about $\frac{1}{4}$ meshed. Then tune VC_2 to receive stations, adjusting VC_1 slightly as necessary to peak up stations. This procedure will minimise the risk of peaking up an image!

2 alternatively, tune VC_2 to a station then adjust VC_1 to a similar setting. Then further adjust VC_1 to peak up signals. Take care to avoid peaking up image signals. This is most common with the oscillator set to low frequencies; the tuning range of VC_1/L_1 is easily wide enough to allow you to get an IF signal from a station higher in frequency than the oscillator signal rather than lower in frequency.

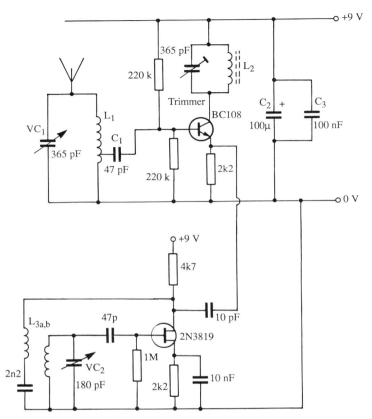

L$_1$ – 25 turns, 1 in diameter.
L$_2$ – 60 turns, 6 in ferrite rod.
L$_{3c}$ – Regeneration winding for FET oscillator.
    Must be phased correctly (see Chapter 5).
L$_{3b}$ – Oscillator winding – 20 turns, 1 in
    diameter on same former as L$_{3a}$

Adjust trimmer for maximum
signal in receiver. Trimmer/L$_2$
tuned to IF

Figure 8.7

If this occurs, you will find that VC$_1$ is probably over half-way unmeshed and VC$_2$ is almost fully meshed. Adjust VC$_1$ until you peak up a signal when more fully meshed; this is the signal *below* the oscillator.

3 whichever method is used, do not forget that the tuning control on

the receiver will give a small amount of fine tuning if you tune slightly away from your chosen IF frequency.

If you suffer from backlash when tuning stations, or a lot of background noise, this indicates that the capacitance of TC_1 is probably a little high; adjust it slightly to reduce the capacitance, whilst still ensuring that stations at the low frequency end of VC_1 and VC_2 can be received. The only other problem that may plague you is hand capacitance; see Chapter 5 for methods of dealing with this. Saying that, the prototype, built as described, gave no such problems. If you wish to couple this converter to a receiver with an aerial socket, L_3 can be omitted and R_4 replaced with a 1.5 k resistor. Connection can be made, via a 10 nF capacitor, to the aerial input of the receiver from the junction of the emitter of TR_2 and R_4.

For those of you with an experimental interest, the circuit in Figure 8.7 will provide further food for thought. Here a FET oscillator is used along with a bipolar transistor mixer.

NINE

Aerials and earths

Whether you have got a simple regenerative receiver or an all-singing, all-dancing digital read-out superhet, the *aerial* system is *the* most important part of a receiving system. Without it a receiver, no matter how good, is useless.

An aerial, often called *antenna*, is a means of converting the electromagnetic field caused by radio waves into an RF voltage that the receiver can convert into audio. In its simplest form, an aerial is just a conductor, the higher and longer the better, connected to the aerial input of the receiver.

Like any electronic component where AC is concerned, an aerial exhibits impedance. This does not mean that an aerial has a fixed resistance of 'n' ohms, though, and you will find an aerial's impedance, as 'seen' by the receiver input, varies when:

1 the frequency used for reception/transmission is changed

2 the place on the aerial at which the connection to the receiver is made (the *feed point* – a phrase from transmitting aerial use) is altered

3 the length and construction of the aerial is varied

4 the aerial is near to other conductors (which may be part of the aerial system) or earthed objects – such as houses, trees, etc.

An aerial acts a little like a tuned circuit, possessing capacitance, inductance, and a little resistance. For this reason, it will also exhibit resonance at a particular frequency, where its efficiency will be greatest. The resonant frequency of an aerial is affected by the factors listed above. The other attribute of most aerials is that they are *directional*; that is, they respond more strongly to signals coming from some directions than others. An aerial that responds equally well to signals from all directions is called an *omnidirectional* aerial.

The feeder

The connection between the aerial and the receiver is called the *feeder*, and for best results we have to ensure that the impedance of the feeder, aerial and receiver input are all fairly similar (see later).

Internal aerials

Let us start by examining the sorts of aerial which are often built-in to receivers.

Ferrite rod aerials

For MW/LW receivers the most common type is the *ferrite rod* aerial. This is a similar arrangement to the MW coil we used in the crystal set, and functions in a way slightly different to that of a basic wire aerial, described earlier: the ferrite rod aerial depends upon the magnetic portion of the radio wave, and the magnetic field is effectively concentrated along the length of the rod. Voltages are thus induced in any coils wound on the rod, and the longer the rod the better the signal pickup. Such an aerial is directional (Figure 9.1) as can be seen by using a transistor portable. Tune it to a weak, fairly distant station, and by rotating the set you will be able to peak up or fade out the signal. Some listeners put their receiver on a rotating cake stand (of the type used when icing cakes) to allow easy rotation! This allows signals in different directions on the same frequency to be separated by nulling out one of them. Although the ferrite rod aerial is specifically intended for use on frequencies below about 2 MHz, some listeners have experimented with ferrite rod aerials up to about 6 or 7 MHz.

Using ferrite rod aerials with external aerials
Some listeners attempt to increase the signal pickup of transistor portables that use ferrite rod aerials on MW by connecting up an external wire aerial. This will nullify the directional qualities of the internal aerial. Connection is not as straightforward as it sounds. These receivers are designed for use with a ferrite rod aerial and common problems when an external wire aerial is used are receiver overload and instability, when whistles will be heard up and down the band and

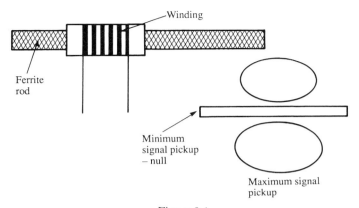

Figure 9.1

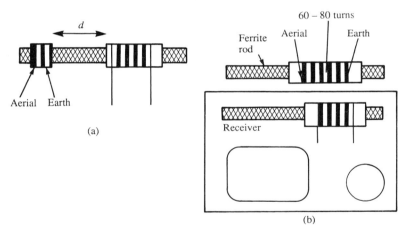

Figure 9.2

some signals, particularly strong local stations, will be effectively un-tunable. If you really *do* want to connect an outside aerial up to such a receiver, a course of action that I do not advocate, *never* connect an aerial wire directly to any of the windings on the ferrite rod. This is almost certain to cause instability, overloading and also some detuning of the tuned circuit. Two approaches can be tried:

1 use a coupling winding of a few turns of wire on a card cylinder that can be slid along the ferrite rod of the receiver (Figure 9.2a). Position it for maximum signal without oscillation or overloading

2 use a separate ferrite rod on the outside of the receiver casing, positioned for maximum signal from the receiver loudspeaker (Figure 9.2b).

It is not usually possible to disconnect the ferrite rod aerial and replace it with another coil to act as a tuning coil so that an external aerial is more easily fitted. Many receivers have ferrite rods fitted as standard on MW/LW, so if you are considering doing a lot of listening on these bands you would be well advised to get a set without a built-in ferrite rod aerial, and use an external long wire/aerial tuning unit combination, active aerial or MW loop (see later).

Telescopic aerials

Most simple SW receivers, particularly portables that also carry the MW/LW bands and the FM band, come complete with a folding telescopic aerial for SW reception. On short wave, these omnidirectional aerials work best when fully extended, but even then are not very efficient. In order to make full use of the low signal strength received by these aerials, the circuits connected to this type of aerial often incorporate high gain. This can lead to problems of a loss of selectivity, especially on the 6 and 7 MHz broadcast bands and an increase in noise level if you try to connect a long wire aerial to the receiver by wrapping the bare end of a piece of wire around the telescopic aerial. These problems are caused by overloading. If your receiver does not have an external aerial socket, and you are forced to use the telescopic aerial as an aerial terminal, then you might like to try the following methods of making the connection.

1 connect the aerial to the telescopic aerial via a variable capacitor, and adjust this for best results

2 use a coupling coil, like that shown in Figure 9.2a, slipped over the telescopic aerial. You will probably need to increase the number of turns a little for best results

3 wrap insulated wire from the aerial around the telescopic aerial a few times. This acts like a fixed, low value capacitor and will reduce the coupling to a level at which overload is not likely.

Metalwork in buildings, such as the steel frames of tower blocks, will have a detrimental effect on the signal strength received by telescopic aerials (or any other aerial mounted indoors in such buildings).

A useful trick is to buy a telescopic aerial from an electronics stockist, solder a length of wire to it and stand it in a window or attach it to the outside window ledge. The wire can then be attached directly to the aerial on the receiver, and this arrangement can help with weak signals.

External aerials

For serious listening, an aerial external to that supplied with the set is often essential. Communications receivers, high class portables and most homemade sets all give best results when connected up to an external aerial (which might be mounted indoors or outdoors, preferably the latter) via their aerial socket. The provision of a socket for external aerials on a receiver makes it possible for the listener to experiment with a great many different aerials to get the best results. Obviously, if your set has both an internal aerial and an external aerial socket, try to use the aerial socket with a decent antenna for best results. One reason for this is that the signal-to-noise ratio for a given signal is usually higher for an external aerial; there is often an awful lot of electrical noise in buildings. There are two main types of aerial connection made available on many receivers; which type you have will be specified in the receiver manual.

Low impedance input
This is usually in the form of a socket and shows an impedance of about 50 ohms to anything plugged in to it. Sockets used on receivers are usually either co-axial types, as seen on the rear of TV receivers, or the more expensive PL256 types which are screw threaded to give a better connection. RCA phono sockets are also occasionally seen. Whatever type of plug is used, the aerial is connected to the centre conductor of the plug and the earth connection to the outer connection.

High impedance input
Some sets have a high impedance input (about 300 ohms) which takes the form of a couple of screw terminals, one for the aerial and one for the earth. This type of socket is suitable for a variety of different aerials, including simple lengths of wire or telescopic aerials.

Feeders and matching

To ensure maximum transfer of signal between aerial and receiver, all impedances in the system should be similar. Thus any aerial linked to the 50 Ω input of a receiver should be connected by 50 Ω feeder cable and the aerial impedance at the feed point should also be 50 Ω. Well, life is not always that simple, and we usually need to *match* our aerial system to our receiver using a device called an *aerial tuning unit* (ATU). Chapter 10 gives details of ATUs. This fits between the aerial feeder and receiver as shown in Figure 9.3 and is adjusted so that the impedance of the aerial/ATU combination at the frequency of interest is the same as the input impedance. The link between aerial system and ATU should be at the impedance of the feeder point of the aerial.

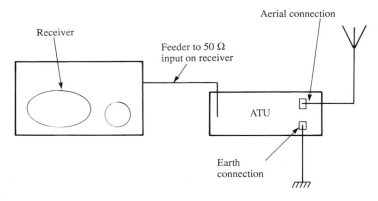

Figure 9.3

Poor matching can lead to the following:

1 overloading by very strong signals

2 increased interference from local electrical noise sources

3 an inability to tune at certain frequencies, known as *deafness*.

The usual feeder to use for 50 Ω connections is 50 Ω co-axial cable, available from most component stockists. The inner copper wire of this cable is connected to the aerial, while the outer braid is connected to any earth connection used. For 300 Ω feeds, 300 Ω ribbon feeder is traditionally used by radio amateurs, though for receive-only set-ups twin electrical flex is likely to work just as well. Feeder cable of 300 Ω is more prone to picking up electrical interference than 50 Ω co-ax.

Whatever type of feeder you use, the following simple rules should be adhered to for best results:

1 always solder the connections between feeders and aerial and earth. Then wrap tightly in waterproof tape

2 when running feeders into the house, keep them as far as possible from any mains wires in the walls, etc. to minimise electrical interference

3 try and keep feeders – especially 300 Ω ribbon – as far as possible from earthed objects. Obviously, at the point of entry you will have to bring it through the wall/window frame/eaves of house or whatever, but try not to trap the cable in any way, say, between a window and its frame.

Long wire aerial

The simplest external aerial is a length of wire – the *long wire* (Figure 9.4a). If you are interested in particular frequencies, then the

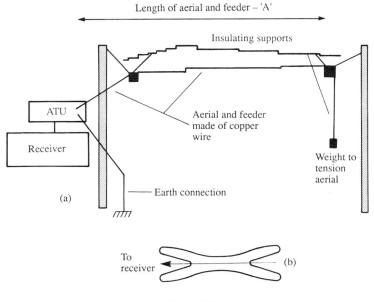

Figure 9.4

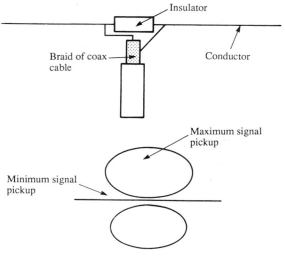

Figure 9.5

aerial wire length should be equivalent to half of the frequency's wavelength. The aerial is directional (as shown in Figure 9.4b) and the directionality depends to a great extent on its length and the frequency on which the aerial is used. On the whole, a length of wire between 10 and 30 metres long, together with an ATU, will give good results on the HF bands. Impedance of such an aerial is quite high, so if an ATU is not used the best connection is probably to the 300 Ω socket of the receiver. A long wire aerial is naturally resonant at λ/2, λ/3 and λ/4 so will be most efficient at frequencies corresponding to these wavelengths. A 20 metre long wire is a popular choice for many SWLs.

Dipole

A *dipole* is another directional aerial which is most efficient at a particular frequency, dependant upon its length (Figure 9.5). A dipole is said to be 'cut' to be resonant at a particular frequency, and it exhibits greater efficiency and directionality around that frequency, thus making the dipole ideal for listeners interested in one band. The impedance at the centre of the dipole at its resonant frequency is quite low, and so 50 Ω co-axial cable can be used to feed the receiver or ATU. A dipole is also quite efficient at 3 times the frequency for which it is cut.

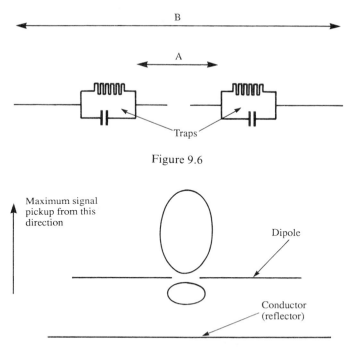

Figure 9.6

Figure 9.7

A variant on the dipole is the *trap dipole* (Figure 9.6). Here the tuned circuits, called *traps*, are tuned to a particular frequency and at that frequency effectively shorten the aerial to length A. At other frequencies, the full length, B, is active as a dipole, thus allowing the antenna to work on two different frequencies.

Antenna arrays

Dipoles are directional all around the central axis. By combining a dipole with other conductors, a directional aerial can be built capable of receiving signals from *one* direction only (Figure 9.7). The aerial is mounted on a mast or tower and is a popular arrangement with transmitting amateurs, but has a few disadvantages for listeners:

1 large gardens and planning permission for the aerial and its mast are often required

2 due to the directional nature of the aerial, a rotator is needed to turn the aerial array to point to the part of the world of interest

3 they are expensive!

MW loop aerials

An alternative type of aerial to the ferrite rod or long wire for the MW listener is a *loop aerial*, which combines the directional qualities of the ferrite rod with the signal pick up of a long wire aerial. In addition, due to the directional properties, interference is reduced – quite a useful property on MW!

Figure 9.8a shows a typical MW loop, consisting of around 100 feet of 36 or 34 swg wire wrapped around a wooden frame. Figure 9.8b

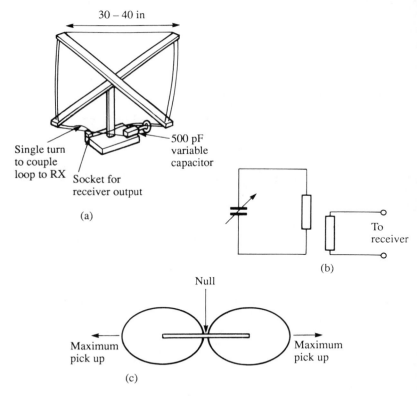

Figure 9.8

shows the equivalent circuit. The 500 pF tuning capacitor allows the loop to be resonated, and the single-turn pick up loop couples the signals received on the loop into the receiver. As this is a fairly high impedance coupling, the 300 Ω input of the receiver should be used.

The greatest signal pickup (Figure 9.8c) is in line with the turns, and the nulls occur when the loop is broadside on to the radio source. In use, a station is tuned in on the receiver and then the loop rotated and the variable capacitor adjusted to bring up the strength of the desired signal whilst decreasing interference and noise. Should it prove difficult to tune stations at the high frequency end of the MW band, you can remove a turn of wire from the loop. If a similar problem occurs at the low frequency end, you can increase the capacitance of the variable capacitor by connecting a trimmer capacitor in parallel with it and adjusting for best results. Loop aerials of this type can be used up to 5 or 6 MHz by adjusting the number of turns on the loop.

Vertical aerials

A simple vertical wire or rod, insulated from earth, will act as an omni-directional aerial. If you use it in conjunction with an earth and ATU, reasonable results are possible.

General points on aerials

1 An aerial should be as high as possible, but should not cross over or under electric cables, phone wires or similar objects. In addition there are rules about aerial heights if you live near an airfield.

2 With long wires, the longer the better is often the best rule. Even if you have to make a bend, try and make the aerial as long as you can. However, do not double the wire back on itself.

3 Keep aerials as far away as possible from earthed objects.

4 Remember that aerials have to support their own weight in a variety of weather conditions, such as strong wind, and that snow will often sit on aerial wires (along with the odd sparrow or something a little bigger!). For this reason, insulated, stranded wire is a good wire for long wire aerials, being flexible and reasonably strong.

5 If you are using directional aerials, do not try and use bearings taken from an atlas using Mercator Projection as a guide for the orienta-

tion that you will use with the aerial. You will need a Great Circle Map centred on the UK. Such maps are available from the Radio Society of Great Britain. Alternatively, a simple computer program can be used to calculate the bearing between two points using their latitudes and longitudes.

6 Use an ATU whenever possible.

7 As a matter of safety, *do not allow aerials to pass under or over power lines or telephone cables*, for obvious reasons.

Earthing arrangements

Several aerials that we have discussed require an earth to be used. The effect of an earth depends upon the frequencies in use and the type of receiver. On the higher short wave frequencies, an earth often makes little difference. However, at low frequencies and with simple receivers an earth is often quite useful, even if it simply prevents hand capacitance on regenerative sets! A few simple rules will give you a good earth connection:

1 the connection between the receiver or ATU and the earth should be as short as possible.

2 do not use a mains earth, water pipe or gas pipe as an earth connection. The latter is illegal, the former potentially dangerous and the second unwise; many water pipes are now plastic!

3 an adequate earth can be made by wrapping wire around one end of a 3 or 4 foot length of copper pipe, soldering and taping it, then burying the pipe in a moist area of earth. Alternatively you can attach the earth wire to chicken wire or similar material and bury that. In dry months, you may need to water the earth to ensure good conductivity between soil and metal. Remember that metals do corrode, though, and an occasional inspection of the earth is a good idea.

Active aerials

An *active aerial* is a system in which the aerial elements are directly coupled to the input of a broadband, untuned amplifier. The difference between an active aerial and an aerial/pre-amplifier combination is

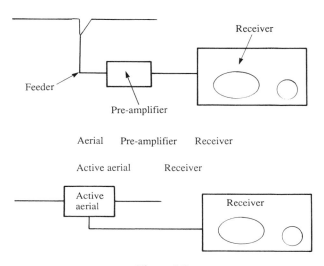

Figure 9.9

shown in Figure 9.9. The active aerial dispenses with the feeder between aerial and pre-amplifier, which improves performance by eliminating signal losses and noise pickup in the feeder. In addition, the feeder can be low impedance coaxial cable – a lot more efficient in electrically noisy places than 300 Ω feeder.

The usual aerial configuration used in an active aerial is a fairly short dipole, much shorter than would be needed to be resonant at any of the frequencies of interest. This will, of course, be relatively inefficient at picking up signals and will offer a fairly high impedance to the input of the amplifier part. However, it will still be directional, and the small signals are amplified by the active part of the aerial to give a small aerial that is directional and as efficient as a dipole at the frequency of interest. Because the amplifier is not tuned, we do not have to fiddle about tuning the aerial for different frequencies.

The big problem with active aerials is that they can overload the input circuits of a good quality receiver. An attenuator between the two, or use of the RF gain control, is useful here.

TEN

Add-ons

The performance of any receiving system can be improved by the addition of simple accessories. Whereas home-made equipment can be modified to suit our requirements, few SWLs are likely to want to try and modify a commercially-made receiver. Fortunately, great improvements can be obtained by circuits which either process the RF signals before they reach the aerial socket of the receiver or by circuits which process the audio signals as produced at the headphone socket output of the receiver. In this Chapter, I will examine some circuits which will help you get the best from your receiver.

The ATU

The *aerial tuning unit* (ATU) is probably one of the most useful accessories a listener can have: it matches the impedance of the aerial system to the input impedance of the receiver, thus ensuring maximum signal transfer between aerial and receiver. In fact, the names *impedance match* or *aerial matching unit*, used by some manufacturers, are more descriptive of what the ATU does. Suitable ATUs are available commercially, though you should not go to the expense of those designed for transmitting systems; they will work just as well for receiving applications but they are much more costly. ATUs are easy to build; Figure 10.1 shows a typical circuit.

Whether commercial or homebrew, ATUs are used in the following manner:

1 tune in a fairly steady signal, then adjust the coil tapping (S1 in the circuit of Figure 10.1) for maximum signal strength. This is often easier on weaker signals, as the signal strength increase is easier to

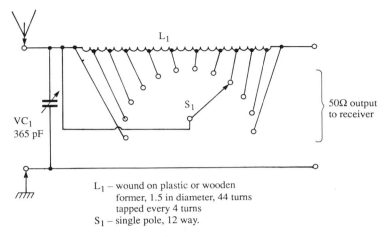

L_1 – wound on plastic or wooden
former, 1.5 in diameter, 44 turns
tapped every 4 turns
S_1 – single pole, 12 way.

Figure 10.1

see. In addition, it helps if you can turn off the receiver AGC whilst adjusting the ATU.

2 peak up the signal with the variable capacitor. Some ATUs have two variable capacitors, and in this case both need to be adjusted.

3 you can make notes of the optimum coil settings for each band, thus speeding up the job in future.

An ATU has a number of effects on signals. First, it reduces the strength of out of band signals reaching the receiver RF input/mixer stages, thus reducing the possibility of overloading and image reception. Second, it maximises signal transfer between aerial and receiver. Finally, it reduces the effects of local interference.

Various combinations of capacitance and inductance will function as ATUs, and it is an area where a little experimentation will work wonders. Even simple arrangements like those in Figure 10.2 may have beneficial effects in some cases.

Preselectors and RF amplifiers

We have already noted that the addition of RF amplifiers to the input of many modern receivers is a recipe for disaster; overloading is the usual result. However, for sets with poor sensitivity a tuned RF amplifier, called a *preselector*, can often improve performance.

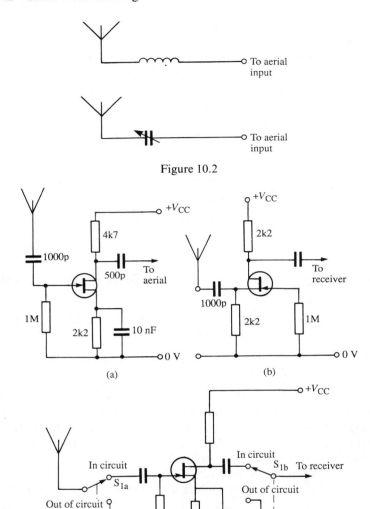

Figure 10.2

Figure 10.3

These circuitrs are particularly useful with older receivers: such receivers tend to be deaf at higher frequencies. The preselector is the best solution, the tuning stage allowing the rejection of out of band signals thus reducing the risk of image reception and overloading. Preselectors should not try to supply too much gain, as overload problems will become more likely. You can get the best of both worlds by supplying some attenuation as part of your aerial system or by allowing the preselector to be bypassed when signals are strong enough not to need amplification.

Figure 10.3 shows typical untuned RF amplifiers, while typical preselectors are shown in Figure 10.4. FET devices are popular in such

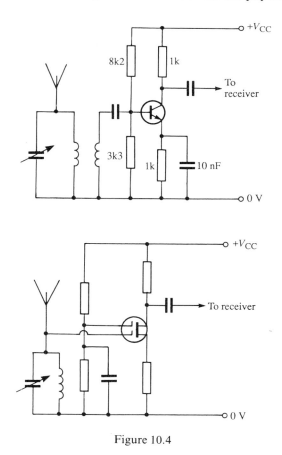

Figure 10.4

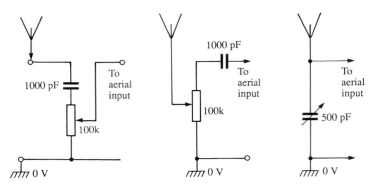

Figure 10.5

applications as they show less tendency to overload than bipolar transistors, though the latter are usually perfectly adequate. Attenuators for use with such circuits can take a variety of forms, such as the ideas shown in Figure 10.5. There are two places to place the attenuator – between the aerial and the preselector/amplifier or between the preselector and the receiver input. The latter is my favourite place; any noise produced by the amplifier circuit is attenuated by the same degree as the signal, thus maintaining the signal-to-noise ratio of the signal that reaches the receiver input. Placing the attenuator between the preamplifier and the aerial would attenuate the incoming signal, but not the amplifier noise. The only advantage to putting the attenuator in this position is that it can be used to protect the preselector from overload, but if signals are that strong, what are you using extra amplification for?

Use of untuned RF amplifier is straightforward; simply turn them on. With preselectors, tune in a signal on the receiver and then peak up the signal with the preslector tuning control. Care is needed, as it is theoretically possible to peak up the image signal on superhet sets, but with a little practice you will soon find out which settings on your preselector correspond to which frequencies on the receiver. Whatever design you use, take care; switch them out of circuit when receiving the 49 and 41 m bands, as overloading is likely, especially in the evening. This is likely on any of the broadcast bands when conditions are right. In addition, remember that any electronic circuit will add a little noise of its own to the signal being received, so noisy preselectors can introduce noise signals which will be amplified by the receiver, causing more background noise.

Frequency measurement

At the heart of any SWL activity is the ability to estimate the frequency to which you are tuned. With home-made sets, frequency estimation is often rough and ready; you can 'guesstimate' the band that you are listening on, and with experience of a particular receiver and a book like the WRTH you can roughly calibrate the set. However, if more accuracy is required then a different approach is needed. Sets have either analogue or digital tuning readouts. The analogue readout is usually in the form of a pointer which moves across a scale whenever the tuning knob is turned, the scale having frequencies marked on it. Digital readouts indicate the frequency as a series of digits. The latter can be accurate to 100 or even 10 Hz in expensive sets. On the other hand, even with some commercial sets, especially the portable receivers that have one or more short wave bands but are not really designed for serious short wave listening, estimating frequency on analogue dials can be difficult.

Calibration charts

A very simple way in which you can interpolate between the frequency points marked on analogue scales is to use a calibration or logging scale. Some receivers have this already; a scale, often 1 to 100, marked on the face of the receiver. This is not a scale in kHz or anything like that, it just allows you to reset the receiver frequency accurately each time to a particular frequency. The problem remains though; what does 56.5 on the logging scale actually mean in terms of kHz?

The solution to this is simple, but requires a little time. For each tuning range on your receiver, select some stations whose frequency is accurately known (either from sources like the WRTH or from 'over the air' announcements) which are spread over the width of the logging scale. For example, you might have a station at 20 on the logging scale, one at 41, one at 63, one at 84 and one at 99. Now get a sheet of graph paper, and label it as shown in Figure 10.6. Plot the points and draw a line through them, the more points the better. A curve of some sort is more likely than a straight line. Now, if a station is heard you can read off its logging scale reading, draw a line up from this point on the graph until it hits the line and then draw a line across to the frequency axis; where the line crosses that axis is the frequency to which you are tuned.

Calibration can be made easier by fitting a larger knob to the tuning control, although this tends to detract from the appearance of the set.

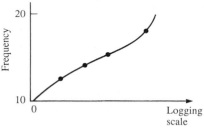

Figure 10.6

In addition, when determining frequency try and do it with the fine-tune control at its calibration setting – usually in the centre of its travel. This ensures that inaccuracies are not introduced by the setting of the fine tune control, which may cause the received signal to be up to a couple of kilohertz away from the frequency recorded on the receiver tuning display.

Using stations with a known frequency is an indirect method of measuring frequency, and we will examine a couple more of these methods shortly. The only direct way of measuring the frequency to which you are tuned is to use a frequency counter to measure the frequency of the local oscillator of a superhet or direct conversion receiver. Of course, with superhets, the frequency counter needs to be able to take into account the IF of the receiver, and various ICs are available that subtract the IF from the local oscillator frequency before displaying it. Frequency counters are not exactly home brew projects, though ready-made modules and kits are available from such companies as Cirkit and Maplin Electronic Supplies.

General points on connecting a frequency counter

The first problem is getting a signal of sufficient amplitude to the counter. If the LO of the receiver is not too well screened, an insulated wire from the input of the FC can be draped around the local oscillator portion of the receiver, with the earth of the FC being connected to the ground of the receiver. Frequency counters often incorporate buffer/amplifier circiuts and so can be quite sensitive, sometimes requiring only a 50 mV or so signal to give good results. Alternatively, the frequency counter may need wiring up to the receiver LO stage. However, this should only be done if you know what you are doing, especially in older receivers where mains voltages may be flying around! With homebrew direct conversion receivers, output to the frequency counter can be via a single transistor buffer stage to minimise the loading effect of the frequency counter input on the oscillator frequency.

The frequency counter power supply, if it comes from the receiver, should be bypassed with 47 nF and 100 μF capacitors to bypass any noise appearing on the power lines; digital circuits like frequency counters are great sources of noise pulses, and can cause severe interference. To eliminate this, the frequency counter should be mounted in an earthed metal box. I find frequency displays that use LCD outputs to be less noisy than LED output frequency counters, which often turn the LEDs on and off very quickly to minimise current consumption. This switching, however, causes a lot of interference. In some receivers, the facility exists to turn on the frequency display only when a reading is actually required.

Frequency meter problems include:

1   interference to the receiver on particular frequencies, often multiples of the clock frequency of the frequency counter. This is minimised by good design and screening.

2   insufficient input signal to the counter may cause random fluctuations of the displayed reading. This is *not* the same as the last digit fluctuation described below.

3   fluctuation of the last digit is usual in digital frequency readouts, and cannot be avoided. However, you should be aware of it; if the display reads to a final position of 1 kHz, then any displayed frequency will be accurate to plus or minus 1 kHz. If, however, the last digit is accurate to 5 kHz, then the frequency tuned in is the displayed frequency plus or minus 5 kHz. Do not rely *too* much on what the frequency counter tells you!

However, frequency counters are well worth having; I would have to think very hard before buying a set without one. You can tune to a particular frequency at which you know a signal will be transmitted and then stay put until the signal is heard – not easy with analogue tuning scales.

Indirect frequency measurement

These revolve around comparing the frequency of an unknown radio signal with that of a locally generated, low power, RF signal.

Using a local VFO

A calibrated variable frequency oscillator (VFO) can be used to calibrate a receiver. You may be able to borrow one, or if you are thinking about doing a lot of radio work they are widely available as RF signal generators. Operation is simple: loosely couple the output of the oscillator to the aerial input of the receiver, set the oscillator to, say, 5 MHz, and tune until you hear the oscillator signal in the receiver. The oscillator output level should be as low as possible and as loosely coupled to the receiver input as possible to avoid problems with receiver overloading and oscillator harmonics. You can then repeat the process for other calibration points on the receiver.

If you have tuned a signal in and you want to know the frequency, tune the oscillator until the oscillator signal is heard along with the radio signal of interest. This is easily recognised if the receiver is not tuned to a station, because the receiver output will be silent (if in AM mode), or will whistle if in SSB/CW mode. On the other hand, if the set *is* tuned to an AM station, the oscillator carrier will be heard as a whistle. The lowest pitch of whistle indicates the same frequency.

This, incidentally, is the principle behind a piece of test equipment called the *heterodyne wavemeter*.

Using a crystal calibrator

A crystal calibrator is an oscillator, based on a quartz crystal for frequency stability, that gives an output at certain frequencies, say, 1 MHz, 100 kHz and 10 kHz, with harmonics of the signals strong enough to be detected up to and beyond 30 MHz. A block diagram of a typical crystal calibrator is shown in Figure 10.7a. The circuit of a crystal oscillator is shown in Figure 10.7b. The 7400 IC is used to generate a harmonic-rich square wave at a frequency of 1 MHz. This is then fed to two divide-by-ten counters to provide outputs at 100 kHz and 10 kHz (Figure 10.7c). The circuit should be built into a metal box, with a socket for output. Three 1.5 V batteries can be used to provide the 4.5 volts power supply. In use, the output of the calibrator is connected loosely to the input of the receiver.

Let us say that the calibrator is to be used to tune to a particular frequency, say, 7.235 MHz. Procedure is fairly straightforward. First, loosely connect the output from the calibrator to the receiver input. This can be done by wrapping a wire from the calibrator output around the aerial input of the receiver, or by using a small (< 5 pF) value capacitor to directly connect the calibrator to the aerial input.

Next, set the calibrator to its 'MHz' switch position and tune for the appropriate harmonic frequency on the receiver. The receiver calibration should be adequate for you to differentiate between 6,7 and 8 MHz 'pips' heard from the receiver. We need the 7 MHz pip. Now, select the '100 kHz' switch setting of the calibrator, and tune the receiver *upwards* in frequency. The first pip heard will be at 7.1 MHz, and the second will be at 7.2 MHz. Once on 7.2 MHz, the '10 kHz' switch setting should be selected and the receiver tuned upwards in frequency to the third pip heard. The receiver is now on 7.23 MHz. The desired frequency of 7.235 will be half way between this marker pip and the next one.

If the calibrator is used to estimate a frequency, operation is a bit different. First, note where the station is on the receiver logging scale. Next, select the '1 MHz' calibrator switch position, and tune *down* in

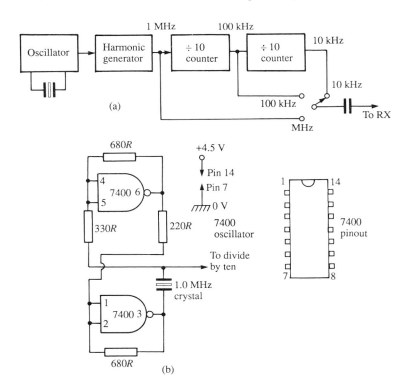

Figure 10.7(a), (b)

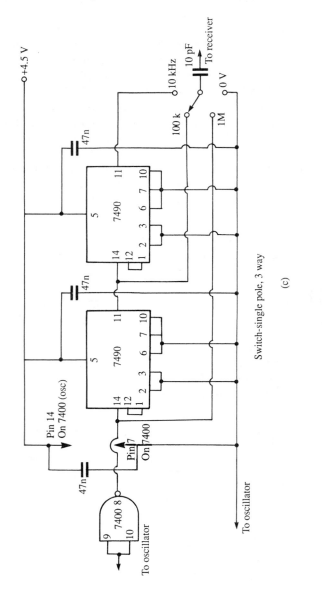

Figure 10.7(c)

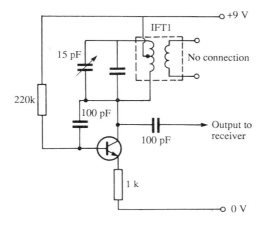

Figure 10.8

frequency until a marker is heard. The receiver calibration must be adequate to tell you which harmonic this is – say it is 11 MHz. Next, select '100 kHz' and tune *upwards* in frequency back towards the signal. Count the marker pips heard, and stop at the last marker *before* the station. You may need to tune through the station to ensure that you have got the last pip. If you do, then simply tune back to it. Say, we counted 4 pips. Finally, select '10 kHz', and tune upwards again, to the marker pip below the station. Say 5 pips are counted. If the calibrator pip and the signal coincide, then our station is on 11 450 kHz. If not, the station is between 11 451 and 11 459 kHz.

The beat frequency oscillator

CW and SSB signals can only be resolved by using some means of inserting a carrier wave (SSB) or generating a beat note (CW). A BFO is a popular means of doing this, and is simply an RF oscillator that operates at a frequency close to the IF of the receiver and that can be tuned above and below the IF. Some receivers feature a BFO as standard for CW and SSB resolution, but others do not. If your set does not, why not build a BFO? A typical BFO circuit is shown in Figure 10.8. IFT1 is a widely available IF transformer, the frequency of operation being selected depending upon the receiver IF. Such transformers include a built-in resonance capacitor. To set up this BFO, tune in an AM signal and then turn on the BFO with an insulated wire running from the BFO output taped to the rear of the receiver. You may find, with well-screened receivers, that the wire needs to be introduced inside the receiver cabinet and taped, carefully, near to the IF stages of the receiver (easily spotted by the 'tin cans' housing the IF transformers. Set VC_1 to half mesh, and turn on the BFO. Adjust the core of the IFT with a suitable insulated trimming tool – a nylon adjuster, filed down plastic knitting needle, but *not* a small screwdriver! – until a beat note is heard and carry on until the lowest pitched note possible is found. Adjusting VC_1 either side of the centre position will cause a whistle on AM, and will allow SSB and CW signals to be resolved, described in Chapter 11.

Audio processing

So far, all the add-ons we have discussed operate at the RF or IF stages of the receiver. Considerable improvements can be made to receiver performance by processing the audio output to reduce interference, increase selectivity and reduce impulsive noise, such as that caused by the switching of electrical circuits.

Receiver audio output

There are three possible sources of audio signal on receivers, apart from the sound coming out of the loudspeaker!

1 *External speaker output.* This socket allows an external loudspeaker of the appropriate impedance to be plugged in, muting the internal speaker. This output is at the receiver audio amplifier's full power level and a low impedance is usual, often $8\,\Omega$ in modern sets.

2 *Headphone output.* Again, this mutes the internal loudspeaker when the headphones are plugged in, and the impedance is usually in the 4 to $40\,\Omega$ region. Level of output is usually high, often taken from the latter stages of the audio amplifier, if not the loudspeaker output.

3 *Auxiliary audio output.* Some receivers offer an output of a few kilohms impedance and about 30 to $100\,\text{mV}$. This is taken from the early stages of the audio chain – or even from the output of the IF stages of the receiver – and when used does not necessarily mute the internal speaker. Whereas the first two outputs mentioned are affected by the setting of tone and volume controls, this one is not.

This is a useful output for add-on devices that contain their own audio sections, such as commercially available filters, etc.

The choice of output to use is up to you to a great extent. If I am using any audio processing circuits, such as notch filters, I tend to use the auxiliary audio output of the receiver and amplify the signal to loudspeaker or headphone strength *after* filtering.

Adding an external loudspeaker

Some receivers do not have a built-in speaker; they come as optional extras! Other receivers, for example the Bearcat DX1000, have a rather small speaker which appears to give a rather 'tinny' response. Considerable improvements can be gained by using an 8 Ω hi-fi speaker as an external loudspeaker, fed from the appropriate socket on the receiver.

Use of headphones

Headphones should be used for all serious listening; apart from cutting out extraneous room noise and so aiding concentration, they prevent the noise from your receiver annoying others. 'This is London' at 3 am at loudspeaker volume will *not* endear you to others!

Most 'phone outputs are capable of driving low impedance (8 to 32 Ω) headphones, but check with the instructions that come with your receiver first. Older receivers require high impedance headphones, or a combination of an impedance matching transformer and low impedance 'phones, as was used in the crystal set in Chapter 4. My personal preference is for cheap hi-fi headphones. Some writers have argued that these phones are 'too good', as they also reproduce the noise on signals. My answer is that noise should be removed by appropriate filters, rather than relying on the headphones to do the job for you!

These hi-fi phones are stereo, and if you were to plug them in to your receiver you would get the signal coming out of one earpiece only. This is not really on, as this is very tiring. There are two solutions; the first is to 'butcher' the phones, removing the stereo plug and rewiring the phones to use a mono plug. The second method is to use a stereo-to-mono jack plug adaptor, widely available from component stockists. This has the great advantage that when conditions are not too good you can still use the phones to listen to Vivaldi on the hi-fi!

Get headphones that are comfortable to wear over long periods. They should be fairly light, with padded earpieces and a padded headband. Most headphones allow you to adjust the position of the ear-pieces on the headband to suit your own requirements. The lead from phones to plug should be as flexible as possible, and long enough to allow some freedom of movement whilst wearing the phones. A coiled lead of about 1 to 1.5 m is adequate. I have found that 'Walkman' style headphones are not really suitable for listening, as they do not cut out extraneous room noise and they can be tiring to wear.

When using headphones, take care! Do not have the receiver volume up too high, or you will be assured of an ear-shattering experience if you tune across a very strong signal! Similar problems arise when someone switches a light or electric motor on or off, or when the central heating starts up. These sources of impulse noise tend to cause anything from a faint click to a loud thump in the phones, and can cause some discomfort – believe me!

Some receivers have noise limiters to prevent this sort of problem, but a simple solution is shown in Figure 10.9 where back-to-back diodes limit the voltage across them to 0.6 V. In use, this circuit sits between headphones and receiver, with the receiver gain adjusted so that the audio is at a reasonable listening level but is not distorting. The noise peaks will then be reduced when they occur. Some readers may recognise this simple noise limiter as being the same arrangement that is used in simple guitar fuzz boxes.

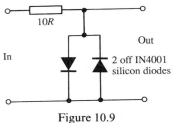

Figure 10.9

Audio filters can also be used to provide some degree of selectivity at the audio stage of the receiver, rather than the IF stage, or to cut out interfering frequencies such as heterodyne tones. There are two types of filter commonly used; the *bandpass* filter, which allows a given range of frequencies only to pass through, and the *bandstop* filter, which attenuates a given range of frequencies.

Band pass filters

These allow us to limit the bandwidth of the receiver at the audio stage.

A filter can, for example, have a bandwidth of around 3 kHz centred around 1.5 kHz, and this would improve selectivity of a receiver for SSB signals by limiting the bandwidth to that required to properly resolve a SSB signal. We can thus effectively provide variable selectivity for a receiver with a fixed IF bandwidth. Typical filter bandwidths and mid-point frequencies might be:

Reception mode	Bandwidth	Centred on
SSB	3 kHz	1.5 kHz
AM	6 kHz	3.0 kHz
CW	800 Hz	600 Hz
NBFM	12 kHz	6 kHz

The receiver can be tuned normally, and an audio filter selected to get the best results. These filters are best driven from the low signal, high impedance output of the receiver, and so need to be followed by some audio amplification to get the signal back up to strength, as shown in Figure 10.10. A low pass filter could be used, with high frequency cut offs at 3 kHz, 6 kHz, 800 Hz or 12 kHz, but the use of bandpass filters allows some of the low frequency signal that contributes to noise but not to the signal to be cut out. Figure 10.11a shows a simple bandpass filter with adjustable bandwidth, formed by the C43140 operational amplifier IC. The centre frequency can be calculated for given resistor and capacitor values by the equation shown, or the centre frequency could be made variable over a range of frequencies by using a dual-ganged linear potentiometer in place of R_1 and R_2. The only point to note when building a filter like this is the split rail power supply, a common requirement in operational amplifier circuits,

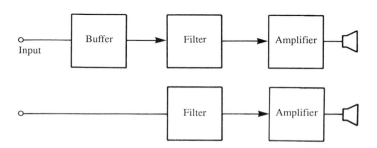

Figure 10.10

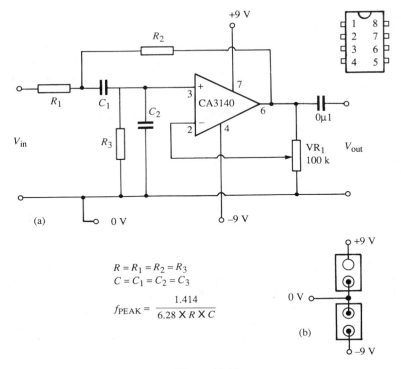

$$R = R_1 = R_2 = R_3$$
$$C = C_1 = C_2 = C_3$$

$$f_{PEAK} = \frac{1.414}{6.28 \times R \times C}$$

Figure 10.11

where two 9 volt batteries are used to provide the power needed by the circuit. This is shown in Figure 10.11b. An audio amplifier, such as the one based on the LM380 featured earlier in the book, could be powered by the battery that provides the $+9\,V$ side of the power supply, $0\,V$ being used as signal return as usual.

Band stop filters

These are often called *notch filters*, and are used to heavily attenuate signals at or around a particular frequency. A common use is to get rid of heterodyne whistles caused by two neighbouring carrier waves. By varying the bandwidth, though, it is possible to notch out larger amounts of interfering signal, but this is not often a practical proposition due to the probability of notching out some of the desired signal. However, a combination of bandpass filter to improve selectivity and a

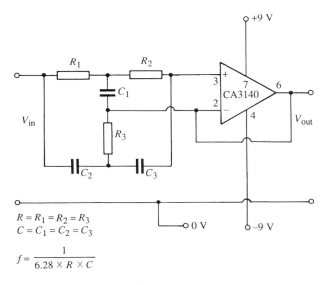

Figure 10.12

notch filter to remove whistles may be very useful indeed. Figure 10.12 shows a notch filter in which the frequency of maximum attenuation is set by the values of the resistors and capacitors as shown. Again, it should be driven from a high impedance output on the receiver (or via a matching transformer from a low impedance output) and the output will need boosting to loudspeaker or headphone level.

Terminal units

If you intend processing CW or RTTY signals from your receiver using a computer, then you will require some form of terminal unit to convert the audio from the receiver into some form of signal that the computer can use. The simplest of these devices consists of a *phase locked loop filter* which will give a 5 V (digital 1) signal when a tone of the correct frequency is present at its input, and a 0 V signal (digital 0) if the tone is absent. These 1 and 0 signals can then be fed to a computer and used to allow the computer to decode CW and RTTY transmissions once the computer has been programmed in a suitable way. A simple terminal unit, which will also serve as a CW filter, is shown in Figure 10.13. The signal of interest is tuned in and the BFO pitch

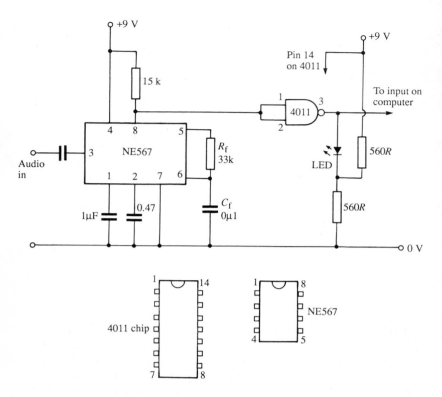

Figure 10.13

adjusted until the LED flashes in sympathy with the signal. The frequency to which the PLL circuit locks can be varied by adjusting Rf or Cf. Increasing the resistance or capacitance will lower the frequency, and vice versa. The circuit as presented will work with either a low impedance or high impedance input, and a medium strength signal. I have been able to read many amateur CW and RTTY contacts using this circuit as the basis of a terminal unit, together with a suitable decoding program on my BBC microcomputer.

Commercially available terminal units range from those only slightly more sophisticated than this to units costing as much as some receivers! The latter types will include their own computer chip and are often capable of displaying the signals on a TV set or printer without the need for a computer, or can send the decoded CW or RTTY signals to a computer for further processing and storage. In addition to CW and RTTY, they can usually decode many other forms of coded transmissions.

Tape recorder output

It is occasionally useful to be able to record off-air signals for some particular purpose. For example, CW signals can be recorded so that you can practice your morse code, or announcements from broadcast stations can be recorded for later study, especially useful if the language is unknown and you are trying to hear a station identification.

On the whole, it is *not* good enough to stand a microphone in front of the loudspeaker of the receiver, as you will pick up a lot of extraneous room noise that you probably did not even realise was in your shack. A direct connection is by far the best proposition – but from where?

Some receivers have a tape recorder output built in so as to make this sort of work easier. This is usually a low signal output taken off before the tone/volume controls of the receiver audio circuits. This output can also be used to drive filters or terminal units when recordings are not being made. If the socket is a 5-pin DIN socket, then a suitable lead between receiver and most tape recorders can be purchased off the shelf. Alternatively, you may have to use the headphone output or external speaker output. This is not as straightforward, as you will need to wire up a lead yourself to connect this output to the MIC input of the recorder. A possible arrangement is shown in Figure 10.14; the capacitor electrically isolates receiver and tape recorder, and two resistors limit the amount of signal reaching the recorder.

However you connect up the recorder, you should run test tapes on different types of signal to see what receiver and tape recorder control

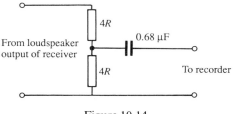

From loudspeaker
output of receiver

4R

0.68 μF

4R

To recorder

Figure 10.14

settings give the best results. If the recorder has a recording level meter, try to adjust the receiver output or recorder input level controls to give a reading of 0 dB on the meter on peak signal strengths, and use manual recording level control on the recorder if you are offered a choice between manual and automatic.

ELEVEN

Using the set

Whatever type of receiver you have got, *operating* the set and knowing how to get the best from it is crucial. In this chapter, I will examine some commercial sets, look at the questions to ask if you are buying a receiver and show you the ways to use the different types of receiver we have discussed to get the best results.

Typical commercial receivers

There are a variety of sets about on the market at the moment, and the main limitation is that imposed by your wallet – sets range from about £35.00 to £3000. An example of a synthesised receiver is the Bearcat DX 1000 receiver, and the Grundig Satelit 1400 is an example of a good quality portable receiver.

There are two main types of set to consider; portable receivers and table-top sets. In each category there are a range of prices and performances, and the first question to ask is 'what will the set be used for?' If you intend doing some broadcast band SWLing, then virtually any reasonable receiver will do. For DX chasing, though, only the better portables and communications receivers will be adequate. For DXing the amateur bands, you will almost certainly need a communications receiver, which incorporates such features as a product detector or BFO for SSB or CW reception, variable bandwidth filters, and so on. We then come to the question of cost. My advice is get the best set you can afford, and pair it up with an appropriate aerial system. Do not forget that some portable receivers do not take kindly to having external aerials connected to them.

When you are considering buying a set, be it new or second hand, do attempt to try it out before parting with your cash, or examine receiver

161

reviews in the radio press. Some chain stores will stock portable receivers suitable for SWLing, but you may find it difficult to test the receiver in the shop, as the telescopic aerial will not give very good results in a metal framed building full of working TV sets and home computers! Specialist shops may provide listening rooms where receivers can be hooked up to an adequate aerial system to give you the opportunity to test the receiver out properly. Whatever type of set you are looking at, it is worth considering the following points.

Frequency coverage

A fairly obvious one, this. Does the set cover the frequency ranges that you want to listen to? In addition, it is vital to have a good method of frequency measurement and it should be easy to reset the receiver to a particular frequency.

Sensitivity

The receiver sensitivity is a measure of its ability to detect faint signals and resolve them into sound. It is not an easy parameter to understand, so I will give a few rules-of-thumb. Sensitivity quoted in the specifications for the receiver should be a few microvolts (the smaller the better) for AM and a value (in microvolts) that is smaller than this for CW and SSB. If there are no quoted specifications, listen around on the 80 and 20 metre amateur bands, you should hear some CW and SSB signals – take an experienced friend with you if you are unsure of what to expect on these frequencies. Whilst on the subject of sensitivity, do not forget that sensitive receivers can be overloaded. Is the RF gain controllable, or are there attenuators that can be switched in to reduce the chances of overload?

Selectivity

The ability to separate stations from one another is clearly important; most good sets will have switchable filters offering differing selectivity. Look in Chapter 10 for typical bandwidths to look for, and try tuning through the bands to see if you can adequately separate the signals heard.

Operating modes

Will the receiver resolve the types of signal that you are interested in?

Aerials

Will the set accept an external aerial? If not, are you happy to use the set with the internal aerial, and will it be adequate for your use?

Outputs

Is the loudspeaker built in? Is there provision for headphones to be plugged in?

Spurious responses

Does the set suffer from image problems or other spurious response problems (see later)? The lower the receiver IF is, the more likely you are to suffer from image problems, especially on the higher frequency bands.

There are more points to consider, of course, but these are a start. You can also get a good idea of receiver performance by examining the reviews that frequently appear in the radio magazines, and in such books as the *World Radio and TV Handbook*.

Some commercial receivers

FRG7, FRG7700, FRG8800 Produced by the Yaesu company, these receivers are very common in listening circles. The original FRG7 was a straightforward, analogue frequency readout, communications receiver whose main drawback was a lack of selectivity (cured by fitting new filters) and a fine tuning control that was not all it could have been. The FRG7700 was better, incorporating a digital frequency readout; still a decent performer. The FRG8800, the currently available receiver from this company, has had a mixed reception. Some users have commented on a lack of senstitivity, but others seem quite happy. All the sets cover the HF bands, with the top part of 10 metres missing on the FRG7. All can resolve AM, CW and SSB, though the FRG7 is not as good as its successors in this respect. In addition, the FRG8800 can resolve NBFM. The FRG7 and FRG7700 are now only available second-hand.

Lowe HF125. This British-built receiver is physically small but very capable, covering 30 kHz to 30 MHz. It will resolve AM, CW, SSB and has optional extras which will allow ECSS and NBFM reception. It is a synthesised receiver, and allows frequency selection by tuning control or pushbutton pad (optional), displaying the frequency on a digital diaplay. The receiver has been well received by listeners, and appears to give good performance.

Sony ICF2001D. Probably *the* portable receiver to have if you need to travel around and do some listening. Covers 150 kHz to 30 MHz, good sensitivity and selectivity and AM, CW and SSB modes. Also accepts an external aerial to replace the telescopic aerial that it comes with.

Vega receivers. Cheap, no frills, middling performance AM portable receivers that cover selected HF broadcast bands. Low IF can cause image problems and selectivity is not too hot. Perfect if you are not sure that you want to shell out a lot of money on a receiver. Cost less than £50.00.

Trio–Kenwood R2000, R5000. Very good, rather expensive communications receivers. Both cover 150 kHz to 30 MHz; well worth a look if you can afford them. These are synthesised receivers, and so include such things as memory and the facility to scan a range of frequencies for transmissions. Will resolve AM, CW, SSB and NBFM. Selectivity, sensitivity and resistance to overloading is good in both receivers.

Bearcat DX1000. This is a reasonably priced synthesised receiver covering 10 kHz to 30 MHz. Selectivity and sensitivity appear good, and it will resolve AM, CW, SSB and NBFM. Now only available second-hand. If you see one, give it a try.

Receiver controls

Let us briefly examine the use of the more common receiver controls. The particular details will, of course, depend upon the receiver in question.

Main tuning. The main features of the tuning arrangement of a receiver should be that it is easy to set the receiver to a desired frequency – i.e. there should be no mechanical or electrical backlash at all – and that the rate of tuning should be slow enough for the modes of interest. For example, a good communications receiver may cover only 20 or 30 kHz in a single rotation of the tuning control, thus making tuning in SSB and CW signals easier.

If the set uses a frequency synthesiser, then the tuning rate is often switchable. My Bearcat DX1000, for example, tunes in steps of either 100 Hz or 1 kHz, the faster rate being used to rapidly scan frequencies and the slower rate used to accurately tune stations in. With a synthesised receiver, a step size of 100 Hz or less is required to accurately resolve SSB broadcasts. Frequencies can often be typed in to synthesised receivers using a keypad, and up and down scanning of frequencies is usually possible at the press of a button.

Most decent sets will also have a means of bandspreading. *Mechanical bandspread* can take two forms; gearing of the tuning control so that several turns are required to cover a given range of frequencies, or use of a separate knob, on the same shaft as the main tuning control, for fine tuning. The latter arrangement is used in the Grundig receiver shown above, where the outer tuning control allows rapid tuning from one end of the band to the other and the inner tuning control allows fine tuning. *Electrical bandspread* is where a separate tuning capacitor, of small capacitance, is provided. This will allow the tuning to be varied by a few tens of kilohertz for a complete turn of the bandspread control. An extreme form of this, where the variation may only be a few kilohertz, is known as *receiver incremental tuning* (RIT) and is most useful for accurately tuning narrow bandwidth transmissions such as RTTY or SSTV.

Changing bands is done, usually, either by: switching, in conventionally tuned receivers or; by typing in a new frequency in synthesised sets. Some sets incorporate preselector or bandset tuning which should be adjusted to the appropriate range whenever the band is changed.

RF/IF gain controls. The RF gain control affects the gain of the stages before the IF stage, the IF gain control sets the IF stage gain. Either or both may be controlled by the receiver AGC. It is often possible, especially on communications receivers to turn the AGC off, thus allowing you to set the receiver gain by use of these two controls. There are lots of ways to do this, but my favourite is as follows. Back off both RF and IF gain controls (or just one if that is all that is available). Then set the receiver volume control to a normal listening level. You should hear a hissing noise. Then advance the IF control to about 75% of full strength (if present) and advance the RF gain control until stations are heard. Then adjust RF/IF gain and volume controls for best results. Obviously, fainter stations will require more RF gain.

Switchable attenuators. In some receivers, switchable attenuators are present rather than RF gain controls. In effect, the set is always at full RF gain but attenuation can be switched in to avoid overload.

Automatic gain control. This provides an automatic means of controlling the gain of the set, so that signals of all strengths come out of the loudspeaker at a similar volume. This can be a bit of a nuisance in some circumstances; for example, a strong station adjacent to a weak station, and reduce the gain of the receiver, possibly supressing the weaker station altogether! For this reason, some AGC systems can be disabled, and the gain controlled manually. AGC settings are said to be either fast or slow depending on how quickly the AGC responds to a signal strength change. Fast AGC is best for rapidly changing signals, such as SSB or rapidly fluttering AM broadcasts.

Filters. Most communications receivers will allow you to vary the bandwidth of the receiver to suit the type of transmission being received. In some sets, the filter bandwidth chosen is set by selecting the reception mode, whilst in others the two functions are separate. I prefer the latter arrangement, as it allows me to use SSB filters for 'winkling out' weaker AM stations between strong broadcasts. Always remember that the wider the bandwidth of the filter, the more interference and noise will get through.

Volume and tone controls. These perform the same tasks as they do on normal hi-fi systems. The tone controls on most receivers are limited to a treble boost or cut function. Treble boost can occasionally make a voice signal more readable, especially one with a limited bandwidth. Alternatively, treble cut can reduce the 'frying eggs' sound sometimes heard on the higher short wave frequencies.

Squelch. A few short wave receivers incorporate a *squelch* control, which is normally only found on VHF/UHF receivers or CB rigs. This can be set so as to mute the receiver audio output when the set is tuned to a quiet channel, but as soon as a sufficiently strong signal appears on the channel the signal will be heard in the loudspeaker of the set. This is a particularly useful feature for monitoring frequencies which may exhibit only occasional broadcasts where the background noise between transmissions can be tiring.

BFO controls. Where a BFO is present, there is usually the facility to select LSB or USB by a switch. Receivers may also incorporate a means of tuning the BFO slightly.

Mode selection. The selection of reception mode – AM, CW, SSB or NBFM – is usually done by a rotary switch or pushbuttons. In some receivers, selecting the mode also selects filter bandwidths, and brings in to play such things as product detectors for CW and SSB. Mode selection may also affect the AGC. For receivers with BFOs, mode selection is usually a means of selecting AM for AM then turning the BFO on for CW or SSB.

S-meter. This gives a visual indication, either by a meter reading or by a bar graph display, of the strength of a signal. S-meters are calibrated in S-points, 1 to 9, with values above that being specified as so many decibels above the level required for S9. Thus a signal of, say, 40 over S9 is very strong indeed. Unfortunately, although there is a standard for S-meter sensitivity, few manufacturers conform to it, so you should not take the meter reading to indicate any *absolute* level of signal. Use it carefully to indicate relative signal strengths.

Memories. Synthesised receivers will often allow the user to store frequently used frequencies and modes in memories for instant recall.

Now we have examined the main controls on the receiver, we can examine how they can be used to resolve signals in the different reception modes.

AM reception

With crystal sets, reception is simply a matter of tuning for the clearest and loudest signal. If conditions are very good, an aerial that is closely coupled to the tuned circuit will probably give rise to overloading, so be prepared to vary the aerial coupling for best results.

With a regenerative receiver, tuning an AM signal is simply a matter of adjusting the regeneration control so that it is just short of the point of oscillation and then tuning carefully. If the bandwidth is too narrow, speech may appear muffled and the signals could be difficult to tune. If this is the case, back off the regeneration control a little. A second method of tuning in AM broadcasts with the receiver in the *oscillating* condition is discussed below under ECSS reception.

DC receivers are not designed for AM reception – most of them are designed and built to cover amateur band frequencies only, where there are very few AM transmissions. However, you can tune for zero beat on an AM signal, and you will hear the broadcast though there is likely to be growling and any oscillator drift problems will become apparent as the oscillator frequency change will cause beat notes to be generated.

With superheterodyne receivers or converters feeding superhets, just tune for the loudest signal. If the receiver is a good quality portable or communications receiver, then we can make use of the additional facilities offered.

A bandwidth of about 6 kHz or less should be used, 6 kHz being quite good for reception of stations with entertainment quality sound.

However, the wider the bandwidth is, the more likely you are to suffer interference. I find that HF broadcast stations can be received quite adequately with a bandwidth of between 2 and 3 kHz. You may find that you have to adjust the tuning slightly away from the listed frequency of a station for maximum clarity – be aware of this fact when you are logging broadcasts.

If the automatic gain control of the receiver can be turned off, then it is a good idea to do so if you are trying to listen to faint stations that are adjacent to very strong signals. If this is not possible, the stronger signal will affect the AGC to such an extent that the weaker signal becomes inaudible. If the AGC is disabled, though, note that fades will be more pronounced and signal strength readings on the S-meter will be more variable. If the signal you are receiving suffers from rapid flutter fading, then your AGC may not be fast enough to cope with it; if available, switch it to a fast position or turn it off and adjust the gain manually.

For signals that suffer from fading and interference, a reception technqiue called *exalted carrier single sideband* (ECSS) is available on certain receivers. Here, AM detection is via a product detector of the type normally used for CW reception, and an AM signal is tuned in as if it were a SSB signal. Even if your receiver has not got this facility, you can simulate it by setting the receiver in the SSB mode and tuning for zero beat, where the heterodyne whistle is at a minimum pitch – usually only a few hertz or even zero. Care is needed with music broadcasts, however; even the slightest inaccuracy in tuning will sound dreadful!

SSB reception

Reception of SSB signals is not possible on a crystal set. On regenerative receivers, the set is at its most sensitive point for reception of SSB signals when it is *just* oscillating. Tune carefully; bandspreading will almost certainly be required on simple receivers unless the tuning range is very small. Hand capacity effects will be particularly noticeable on SSB reception and the methods mentioned in Chapter 5 should be employed to reduce such problems. On regenerative receivers, there is no setting for LSB and USB; just tune through a sideband signal until it becomes audible.

With DC receivers, SSB is quite simple to resolve; again, the set does not mind whether you are receiving an LSB or USB signal, and tuning through the signal will eventually resolve it.

SSB reception on superheterodyne sets is usually limited to the more expensive portables or communications receivers, as a suitable product detector or BFO is required. For this reason, many receivers that cover short waves, such as some of the Russian Vega portables, do not cover the amateur bands. However, if the set covers amateur bands and does not have built in means of resolving SSB broadcasts, there are two ways to get results. First, a BFO can be built and used with the set as described later. Alternatively, a second transistor radio – a Japanese MW tranny, for example – can be used as a BFO. Stand the second receiver next to the shortwave set tuned to an SSB broadcast, and tune the second receiver. At some frequencies on the second receiver the SSB will become audible on the SW receiver. I used this technique when I started listening on HF to resolve 15 metre band amateur stations. This method requires that the oscillator of the second receiver tunes around the IF of the main receiver – it may not work with all combinations of receivers.

Sets with a product detector

In these receivers, switches on the front panel will allow you to set the reception mode to LSB or USB. There will be no separate BFO tuning control, and tuning is by selecting the relevant mode and tuning the receiver until the SSB is resolved.

Sets with BFOs

It does not matter whether the BFO is an add-on or part of the set. Some receivers have USB/LSB switches, which basically turn on the BFO and switch it to the appropriate side of the IF. A *clarifier* control may be available which allows the BFO to be tuned, thus allowing you to control the pitch of the tuned signal. Other receivers simply have a BFO on/off switch and a BFO tuning control which when tuned one way from a central position will resolve LSB and when tuned the other way will resolve USB. Tuning is by adjusting for maximum signal strength then adjusting BFO pitch to get maximum readability.

On the whole, LSB broadcasts will be heard on the amateur bands below 10 MHz and USB will be heard on the bands above this frequency. If you are using a set with a BFO, it is a good idea to turn the AGC off, as the BFO signal can often be strong enough to cause a significant reduction in the strength of the desired signal. If the AGC is off, audio gain can be set fairly high, and RF and IF gain adjusted to bring the desired station up to readable levels. If you cannot turn off the AGC, set it to fast operation if the receiver has it.

Bandwidth should be kept somewhere in the 2.5 to 3 kHz range wherever possible to reduce adjacent channel interference.

CW reception

Much of what has been said about SSB reception is true about CW reception. Again, if possible turn the AGC off and select as narrow a bandwidth as you can. A CW signal will produce two sidebands, one either side of the carrier, and you should tune the one that gives the minimum intereference. If you need the frequency of a CW station, tune to zero beat (between the two sidebands) with the BFO control (if present) at its centre position. The frequency read from the receiver dial will be that of the CW carrier.

NBFM

NBFM signals are unlikely to be heard on a crystal set due to the insensitivity of the equipment. They can be resolved on regenerative receivers by tuning them as AM signals using the *slope detection* technique, in which the receiver is tuned to the strongest signal, ignoring how funny it sounds, then tuned off to one side or the other until a reasonably clear voice is heard. However, the bandwidth will need to be fairly wide. NBFM signals cannot be resolved with DC receivers.

With superheterodyne receivers, few sets have NBFM fitted as standard, and in the majority of cases the signal is tuned in by slope detection, after selecting AM-reception mode.

On the 10 metre amateur band, you are likely to hear FM signals from amateur stations. A wide bandwidth – around 12 kHz – is required for best results but you will hear signals, although sounding a little muffled, with a bandwidth of between 6 and 10 kHz. Bandwidths of much less than this will give unusable results.

RTTY reception

I use the methods outlined above for CW reception, although receiver stability must be very good – regenerative sets and DC receivers will probably *not* be good enough for RTTY reception. Disable the AGC where possible and adjust tuning of the receiver or BFO until a signal is indicated on the terminal unit. Set the receiver into LSB mode or tune the BFO to the position used for LSB reception.

Overloading, images and spurious signals

We have already seen a superheterodyne receiver is prone to image reception and spurious signals, and how most sets are prone to over-loading. We have also seen possible cures to some of these problems. However, to finish this chapter I will indicate how you can recognise overload, image reception and spurious signal problems.

Spurious signals

The first step is to examine any reviews or literature about your receiver. You may well find references to spurious signals there. Other-wise, disconnect the aerial (or close up the telescopic aerial), tune the bands and listen. On some sets, you may still hear faint broadcasts, especially if the receiver has a plastic case, but you are really listening for rushing or whistling sounds that do not increase in volume when the aerial is reconnected. These are signals generated by the receiver. Harmonics of the local oscillator or BFO can cause these problems, so do the test with the BFO on as well. In addition, digital frequency readouts can cause spurious responses, so turn that on as well. Note the strong ones so that you do not waste time in future listening to them. The weaker ones will probably not be heard under normal band condi-tions. If there appears to be a great number of strong spurious responses, then the set may need attention.

Other spurious signals include those generated by crossmodulation, either ionospheric or in the receiver. These can often be recognised by virtue of the fact that the setting of the ATU will affect them differently to nearby real signals on the band, particularly where the mixing is of two strong stations that are on greatly differeing frequencies.

Overloading

Spotting overloading is easy *once you have heard a non-overloaded set on the same band!* Look for a general increase in background noise or untuneable signals. Try decreasing the RF gain control of the receiver or putting attenuation between the receiver input and the aerial. An ATU will also help.

Image reception

Usually fairly straightforward; if a station is appearing where it should not add or subtract twice the IF of the receiver to the frequency tuned; chances are this will be the fundamental of the signal being heard. My Bearcat DX1000 has just one image, due to its high IF (40.455 MHz): it is of the local FM station, Radio Hallam!

Harmonics

Harmonic signals are not easy to recognise, especially if they fall within other broadcast bands. If you think you have got a harmonic, divide the frequency by two and check a source such as the *World Radio and TV Handbook* for a fundamental; then try dividing the original frequency by three. Do not forget that due to propagation the harmonic might be heard when a fundamental signal cannot!

Summing up

To conclude this chapter, operating the receiver is a matter of experience; try out all the knobs and buttons on the set and see what they do. It took me a while to get the best out of each receiver I have ever used, and my log books reflect this fact. Tune in a strong signal, and start playing!

TWELVE

What can you hear?

In this chapter we will take a look at the types of signals that you can expect to hear in the radio spectrum. As short wave listeners, we can split all the different signals that are audible into a number of groups.

Broadcasting stations

These are radio stations whose outputs are designed for entertainment, education or propaganda purposes. At the time of writing, virtually all broadcast stations use amplitude modulation.

Amateur stations

These transmit signals between people who have obtained a license which permits them to operate a radio transmitter from their own homes. Amateurs use a variety of methods of modulating their radio signals, including CW, SSB, RTTY and NBFM.

Time and frequency stations

These are stations which transmit time signals and other technical information. The frequency on which they operate is fixed and very precise. The information is often coded as a series of pulses, with station identification using CW or SSB.

Personal radio services

Between 0 and 30 MHz certain frequencies are used for such things as Citizens' band radio, radio control. On UK CB radio, NBFM is used.

Utility stations

These stations constitute the vast majority of signals heard on a short

173

wave receiver. They include such things as transmissions between shipping and shore stations, aircraft and airports, weather information,
press services, military radio services, radar systems and a host of other
applications. These stations use a variety of modulation methods, CW,
SSB and RTTY being the most common though with other, more
sophisticated methods of putting information on to a radio wave also
being used.

Clandestine, pirate and unknowns

We have all heard of the pop pirates; commercial radio stations
anchored in international waters. These stations are illegally operated
by their owners.

A much greyer area is that of the clandestine station. These are
stations whose political viewpoint differs from that of the recognised
government in the country at which the broadcasts are aimed; to such
an extent that the radio station is operated from outside that country or
from within the country under conditions of great secrecy. The
unknown stations are those I have great difficulty in classifying as
anything else! They include stations that broadcast seemingly endless
lists of numbers and CW transmitters which broadcast one letter continuously.

Accidentals

These are signals that are not intended to be there at all! They can be
caused by receiver defects, in which case the signals are produced by
your receiver (see Chapter 10), or faults at the transmitter, in which
case signals are transmitted on frequencies other than those intended.
There are other effects that can cause these accidentals, as we will
shortly see.

Try a small experiment; tune your radio across a few megahertz of
the spectrum. Do you notice anything about the distribution of radio
signals? Well, you should have noticed that broadcast stations are
gathered together in groups in different parts of the radio spectrum,
rather than being distributed evenly around all frequencies.

This is true of *all* the different types of signal mentioned above. They
are gathered together into *bands*, each band containing signals of the
same general type. In Chapter 13 we will look at the different bands in
some detail.

Before we go on to look at listening to some of these different types of signal, let us take a quick look at UK law and how it affects our hobby.

Listening and the law

It may come as something as a surprise to you, but we in Britain are not legally permitted to listen to all the various signals that we can hear on our radio receivers. The law of radio is enshrined in two documents. These are the *Wireless Telegraphy Acts* of 1949 and 1967, and are quite complex pieces of legislation, so I have tried to extract the essence as far as short wave listening is concerned.

The British government department concerned with radio regulations is the *Radio Regulatory Division of the Department of Trade and Industry*. It is a busy department, dealing with all aspects of radio communications with the exception of broadcasting (BBC, IBA) which is the responsibility of the *Home Office*.

We can only listen to stations in three classes without any special licences: broadcast stations; licensed amateur radio stations; stations acting as frequency standards or giving time signals.

Of course, you may find yourself accidentally listening to broadcasts that are not in any of these categories as you tune from band to band. British law states that if anything should be accidentally heard that you are not entitled to hear, then you should not attempt to profit from that information, nor should you pass the information on to anyone else.

Stations that do not fall in to any of the above groups, then, should not be listened to or reported on to magazines, etc. if they are heard, unless the listener has a licence.

You may wonder how such cases of illegal reception are proved by the authorities. I have no idea, but there were four convictions for the offence in the financial year 1985/86! (*Radio Regulatory Division Annual Report, 1985/86*).

Special licences

Certain broadcasts which you are normally not allowed to listen to are covered by special licences which can be purchased.

Weather stations
A considerable amount of information is transmitted daily from many stations, worldwide, betwen 0 and 30 MHz about the weather. It would

appear that it is not just the British who have an interest in the subject! Seriously, though, it is intended for use by aviators and seamen. The information is typically transmitted as RTTY or FAX signals. To get a licence for the reception of such broadcasts, you must write to the *Meteorological Office* in Bracknell and detail the broadcasts that you intend listening to and what you are going to do with the information. The licence actually comes from the DTI and will cost you £5.00. It is a once-and-for-all payment and does not have to be annually renewed.

Press stations

The press agencies of the world, such as Tass, Reuters, UPI all broadcast over radio links using RTTY. You cannot read these signals without a licence. The DTI will issue such a licence provided that permission has been obtained from the press agency involved.

Unintentional radiation of signals

That is the situation as far as listening is concerned. The other aspect of the *Wireless Telegraphy Acts* that concern us relates to radiation of radio signals. Of course, it is *totally* illegal to transmit *any* sort of radio signal deliberately unless you are permitted to do so, i.e. you are a licensed radio amateur, CB operator or are using radio control equipment.

However, it is possible to broadcast radio signals accidentally! These come from our receivers when any part of the circuit is oscillating at a radio frequency. Three types of set which may generate signals, albeit very weak, are: regenerative receivers; direct conversion sets; converters or superheterodyne sets.

We should do all we can to prevent signals from these sets 'escaping' into our aerial and so being broadcast. Although weak, they could cause interference in some circumstances, and the legislations specifically forbid causing interference to radio services in this way. It also states that we should prevent any signals getting into the mains wiring of our houses, as in this case the mains wiring could act as an aerial and broadcast the signal!

For the short wave listener, that is about it. On higher frequencies, used by television or weather satellites in space, there are more rules concerned with the reception of these broadcasts. However, that is beyond the scope of this book. Readers in countries other than the UK are advised to seek information relevant to their own country should they wish to listen to weather stations, etc.

Listening to broadcast stations

The broadcasting stations are the simplest transmissions to listen to, as they use AM and many of them are intended for reception by world wide audiences. Indeed, many broadcast stations can be received using simple crystal sets, like those shown in Chapter 4. The frequency bands used by broadcasters are detailed in Chapter 13. In this section, we will look at how we can identify a particular broadcast station once we have received it.

There are two types of broadcast station; *international broadcasters* and *domestic broadcasters*.

International broadcasters

These are stations, usually operating in the short wave bands from 5.9 MHz upwards, whose transmissions are intended for an audience abroad. Different bands are used at different times of the day, depending on conditions (Chapter 13). International broadcasters can be characterised in a variety of ways.

1 broadcasts are made in a variety of languages, and the transmissions are beamed, i.e. directed to particular parts of the world at different times of the day

2 times are often given in GMT or UTC (see later)

3 the broadcasts are often less than 1 hour long

4 the content of the broadcasts is likely to be aimed at listeners in foreign countries.

The audiences of such stations vary from expatriates or foreign workers to short wave listeners. Some stations broadcast all day in English, while running other languages on other frequencies. These stations are intended to be received abroad; the powers used are often in the hundreds of kilowatts and large arrays of aerials are used to get the maximum possible signal into the part of the world that the broadcast is intended for. Reception is intended to be by simple equipment as well as complex short wave receivers, and so a good strong signal is desired by the broadcaster. With many international broadcasters, such as *Voice Of America* or *Radio Moscow*, it is quite an achievement to *avoid* hearing their signals!

Domestic broadcasters

Domestic broadcasters, on the other hand, are a different kettle of fish. We are all familiar with some domestic broadcasters; our own BBC *Radio 1, Radio 4,* or our local stations, for example. Domestic broadcast stations produce programmes for local or home country consumption. The powers and frequencies used are intended to give good coverage over relatively small areas but are not intended for reception overseas. Typically, domestic stations on HF are to be found below 10 MHz, with a large number of them in the 90, 75 and 60 metre bands. In general, domestic broadcast stations follow a number of 'rules':

1 programmes are in the main language or dialect of the region. Foreign language programmes are rarely, if ever, broadcast by domestic broadcast stations.

2 times are usually given in local time

3 the power used by such stations is quite small; tens of watts to a few kilowatts with simple aerials

4 whereas international stations, attempting to get world-wide coverage, have a range of frequencies, domestic broadcasters usually stick to one frequency. For their intended local audience, changes in conditions do not often cause serious reception problems.

Whether on medium, long or short wave, receiving domestic broadcast stations is more difficult but much more satisfying than receiving signals from the international broadcast stations. A knowledge of local languages can be a great help but as a source of alternative news or ethnic music, domestics can be fascinating. Of course, do not expect good signal strength!

In Europe and North America most domestic broadcasting is done on medium wave (Chapter 14) and the VHF bands, between 88 and 108 MHz in most places or between 60 and 80 MHz in Eastern Europe. However, in Africa, Southern and Central America, Asia and Australasia, domestic broadcasting is also carried out on the short wave bands, primarily due to the size of countries or geographical problems.

Domestic short wave stations are of great importance in many developing countries, providing mass communications throughout a country that may be geographically difficult to travel over. In addition, some degree of standardisation of spoken language can be achieved through the medium of radio. As broadcast satellites become more and more common, the use of the short wave bands will decrease, but until then they will continue to link the peoples of a country together.

Equipment

We have now got a rough idea of the broadcast stations that we will be able to hear. What equipment do we need? Well, any receiver will pick up a few broadcast stations, even a simple crystal set. However, to get good reception of stations, especially the domestic broadcast stations, we need either a good portable set or a communications receiver. Chapter 11 looked at some suitable sets. However, very good results can be obtained with simple superheterodyne sets, converters or regenerative receivers. Whatever receiver you use, the following points should be borne in mind. You will require good sensitivity and selectivity, good performance in the presence of strong signals and accurate frequency readout.

You will also need a decent aerial. In addition, some of the extras mentioned in Chapter 10 such as a tape recorder, aerial tuning unit and notch filter can be most useful.

Listening techniques

Listening to broadcast stations can be very simple; set up the radio, spin the dial and away you go! However, a more organised approach is advised to get the best results from your listening times.

The first thing to do is to learn how your receiver works, and how to get the best out of it! I cannot emphasise enough, how important it is to know how to get the best performance from your set. A simple set, used by someone who knows how to get every ounce of performance from the equipment, can give a better set, used by an inexperienced operator, a run for its money! If you use the techniques I outlined in Chapter 11, you should have little difficulty in getting good performance from your equipment.

Time and frequency

Even a whizz around the dial will allow you to hear the stronger stations, no matter where you tune and at what time you listen. However, a little thought will improve your chances of hearing signals.

First of all, remember that the broadcast stations are arranged in bands, and that different bands are used at different times of the day and year (Chapters 13 and 14). The bands to listen to also depend upon the geographical areas of interest. Although international law dictates the frequencies to use, some stations do operate outside recognised bands or on the edges of broadcast bands. However, the vast majority of broadcast stations operate within the broadcast bands, so you are much more likely to receive stations if you are tuning through these bands rather than tuning across a set of frequencies outside the broadcast bands.

A knowledge of radio signal propagation can be very useful. Chapters 13 and 14 will give you enough information on propagation and the bands used by broadcasters to allow you to make the best of your listening time.

In addition, political or religious events may affect the timing or content of programmes from different parts of the world. Take two examples; in recent years the death of various Soviet leaders has caused a change in programming of radio stations in the USSR. Also, the Islamic festival of Ramadan causes changes to the programming of many radio stations in Islamic countries. Other, more dramatic activities, such as political upheavals, natural disasters or war can all cause changes in the strength, quality and content of programming from radio stations.

DXing

Listening to stations that are a considerable distance away, are very weak or are not expected to be audible in your part of the world at that time and on that frequency is called *DXing*. What constitutes a *DX* station is a matter of debate in SWL circles; historically, DX stood for Distance eXtra. In those days, to receive a station that was distant from the receiver was something of an achievement. Today, with the international broadcasters running hundreds of thousands or even millions of watts into sophisticated aerial arrays, sheer distance is not a problem. After all, you can pick up *Radio Australia* any day of the week in Europe!

No, I consider that DX stands for *difficulty*. This is not an original viewpoint; it has been around for several years and I believe it was first suggested by a British radio amateur. For a European listener, a low powered station situated in Africa may be considered to be DX whereas a station in Australia on a higher power would not necessarily be DX. Another aspect to consider when we are trying to decide whether a signal is DX is whether or not the signal is *intended* for us to hear. If it is not, then we might easily define it as DX; if the signal is being transmitted from the distant station with the intention of it being heard in our country or area, then it is not really DX.

If you intend DXing rather than listening to high powered stations, then a good receiver and aerial is essential, along with patience and an ability to stay awake at nights! Let us now look at some points to bear in mind when DXing or just listening.

Up to date information

Some of the books and magazines listed below will offer you valuable information on what stations are operating, where and when.

Propagation

A knowledge of propagation, no matter how small, is essential for serious DXing. The information in Chapters 13 and 14 will get you started.

Headphones

The use of headphones is an extremely good idea. Apart from screening your ears from outside noise, they allow you to operate your receiver at unsociable hours. The squeaks and squawks obtained whilst looking for a weak station buried under many other radio stations may be music to your ears but will prevent other members of your household, and possibly neighbouring households, from sleeping!

Tuning your receiver

The skills discussed in the last chapter will be invaluable here. The main thing to remember is to tune slowly, especially if you are looking for weak stations. In addition, though, the following tricks can be usefully employed.

Band checking
Carefully note everything you hear on a particular band. Then if anything odd turns up you will spot it. Tedious, but can be useful.

Band edges and between channels

It is a good idea to tune around the edges of the recognised broadcast bands. Stations can occasionally be found there. If you can select a narrow bandwidth IF filter on your receiver, then try tuning *between* the channels within broadcast bands. You occasionally find low powered domestic broadcasters there. However, your receiver must be *very* selective to allow the desired DX to be received without also receiving sidebands from the adjacent channels.

Heterodynes

Most of the time heterodynes are a nuisance, but we can make use of them for DXing. A weak carrier in close proximity to another station can cause a heterodyne to be heard *even before the weaker station is audible*. Even if there is not a nearby station to generate a heterodyne with the weak station, there is a trick we can apply to simulate one. We simply use the BFO of our receiver. Any AM carrier will show up, as we tune it, as a whistle. If you are using a regenerative set, a similar technique can be used if you adjust the set so that it is just beyond the point of oscillation. You are probably thinking that we have mentioned something like this before; well, you are right. In Chapter 11 we covered the technique of ECSS reception which is quite similar.

Use of frequency meters

Armed with a source of information about stations (see below), we can set our receiver to the frequency of interest with no difficulty if we have got an *accurate* means of measuring frequency. We have already seen a variety of ways of doing this. However, do not forget that even if we are on the correct frequency at the correct time, the desired station may not be heard due to propagation difficulties. The word here is *patience*! Fading of broadcasts can be very slow, a single fade taking several minutes or even tens of minutes to complete, particularly on the lower frequencies. So, stay on channel and tune carefully around the stated frequency of operation of the station. Some stations, particularly from developing nations, have rather poor frequency control and stations have been known to operate several tens of kilohertz off frequency on one occasion and then be back on frequency the next day.

AGC control

If you are trying to tune in a weak signal in close proximity to a strong one, then the automatic gain control of your receiver may give you some problems. In particular, the AGC will follow the louder signal and thus the weak signal will probably be made even weaker!

Alternatively, when two stations are heterodyning with each other, the beat frequency produced will cause the AGC to operate in sympathy with the beat note rather than either signal.

In either of these situations, turn the AGC off and use the receiver RF and/or IF gain controls to adjust the gain of the receiver.

Use of accessories

The various add-ons mentioned in Chapter 10 can all make life easier. A common problem is overloading, especially on the lower frequency bands. Use of preselectors and attenuators can prevent problems here and audio filters and noise limiters can cut down interference problems.

Identifying stations

Once we have tuned in a station, the next part of the job is identifying it. The main tools for identification are sources of up-to-date information and reasoning of the type used by Sherlock Holmes. Let us start by looking at three books that are available and list station information. All the views expressed in this section reflect my own personal opinions of the books and magazines.

World Radio and Television Handbook

Known as the WRTH, this book is a must for the serious DXer or listener. It contains lists of stations by country and frequency, giving details of times, frequencies and languages used, along with the address of the station and other invaluable information. It is published annually by *Billboard* and is distributed in the UK by *Pitmans*, but is probably available via any large bookshop. You do not need to buy a new copy each year; I buy a new one once every two or three years. This is just as well, because it is not cheap (£17.95 for the 1988 edition). However, if you can afford it, you should not be without it.

Guide to Broadcasting Stations

This useful little book, published by *Heinemann–Newnes*, has lists of stations by frequency, some useful addresses, and some chapters of useful information to the SWL. Though not as detailed as the WRTH, it is good for a listener on a budget.

Passport to World Band Radio

Similar in content to the WRTH, though without the detail, this covers the frequenices between 2.3 and 21.5 MHz. This does encompass the frequencies commonly in use at the time of writing but the other two books detail stations outside this frequency range. Also features a buyers' guide to receivers. Available from *Interbooks*, this was previously in two volumes called *Radio Database International*.

As with many things in life, you pays your money and you takes your choice! My personal preferences are for the WRTH and the Guide to Broadcast Stations.

Even if a book is published on an annual basis, changes do occur between publications. For this reason it is a good idea to subscribe to magazines or DX club newsletters. A list of currently active DX clubs is to be found in Appendix 1, so it may be a good idea to contact them and see what member services they offer. As to magazines, my personal favourites from the UK scene are listed here.

Short Wave Magazine

A 'grand old man' of the British radio magazines, that recently celebrated its 50th birthday by being bought by the *Practical Wireless* people. SWM now caters for the listener almost entirely, and features useful articles as well as information on what's on the bands in its *Seen and Heard* columns.

Practical Wireless

Now catering mainly for the amateur radio operator, but still featuring information of use to the SWL, especially if you are concentrating on listening to amateur signals.

Radio and Electronics World

This magazine has regular news and information about short and medium wave listening, along with the occasional constructional article of immediate use to listeners.

Other magazines that might be worth a look at on the UK market are *Amateur Radio* and *Ham Radio Today* which are both aimed more at the radio amateur rather than the listener. However, they have useful articles, especially the latter which features an occasional listeners' column; *Listening on*. The magazine *Everyday Electronics* also features occasional radio-related constructional articles. There are also a variety of specialist short wave listening magazines which are difficult to get hold of in this country, such as *Popular Communications*. In addition, some broadcasters such as the BBC *World Service* and *Radio Nederlands* (the Dutch international broadcast service) produce leaflets that are of use to listeners and DXers.

DX programmes

Many broadcasters on the short waves include programmes on short wave listening and DXing in their schedules. These programmes, typically half an hour's duration, broadcast in a variety of languages including English, give you up-to-date information on what can be heard in different parts of the world, often based on the reports of other short wave listeners. I make use of these programmes to annotate the frequency listings in my WRTH.

I am not going to list these programmes here; schedules change quite quickly and so any information printed would be obsolete quite soon. However, a list can be found in the *Guide to Broadcasting Stations* and information about these programmes can be obtained from the broadcasters themselves.

The first step in identifying a station is to get the frequency of operation and the time as accurately as possible. The frequency side of things depends on the receiver, and getting an accurate measurement of frequency was covered in Chapter 11.

Time

SWLs use the 24-hour clock format for recording time, and always base their time measurements on Universal Coordinated Time (UTC). This, by the way, is the same as Greenwich Mean Time (GMT) which you hear mentioned still on the BBC *World Service* and a few other international broadcasters. A few stations may be heard quoting times using 'Zulu' e.g., 'Eight hours Zulu'. This is the same as UTC.

This removes any ambiguity of time due to the use of local time; for example, British Summer Time is 1 hour ahead of GMT, and the local times in different countries can be several hours ahead or behind UTC. Try and measure time to the minute; any further accuracy is rather pointless. Whatever timepiece you use should, of course, be correct. The best way to check it is to use the time pips broadcast by the BBC or other stations.

Midnight UTC is 0000 hours, 12 noon is 1200 hours and 11 pm is 2300 hours. Minutes are always quoted as minutes past the hour. So, let us take a couple of examples of converting times into UTC. British Summer Time 3 minutes past 12 noon is quoted as 1103 hours UTC, remembering that BST is 1 hour ahead of UTC. GMT 4 minutes to midnight is quoted as 2356 hours UTC.

Time can give you a useful indication of the location of the station you are listening to, if the station gives the *local* time as part of its announcements. Table 12.1 shows the variation between local time and

Table 12.1 Time differences between local time and UTC.

This list is by no means comprehensive. A fuller list is given in the *Guide to Broadcasting Stations* or the *WRTH*. In general, for every 15° east of Greenwich, add 1 hour to UTC. For every 15° west of Greenwich, deduct 1 hour from UTC.

Country	Local Time (+ or − UTC)
Alaska	−8
Albania	+1
Algeria	+0
Argentina	−4 (−3 in summer)
Ascension Islands	0
Australia	+8 to +11
Austria	+1
Azores	−1
Bahamas	−5
Belgium	+1
Bermuda	−4
Bolivia	−4
Brazil	−3 to =5 (−2 to −4 in summer)
Bulgaria	+2
Cameroon	+1
Canada	−3.5 to −9 (−2.5 to −8 in summer)
China	+8
Cuba	−5
Czechoslovakia	+1

Table 12.1 (cont.)

Denmark	+ 1
Ecuador	− 5
Egypt	+ 2 (+ 3 in summer)
Finland	+ 2
France	+ 1
Gabon	+ 1
Germany	+ 1
Greece	+ 2
Holland	+ 1
Hungary	+ 1
Iceland	− 1 (0 in summer)
India	+ 5.5
Israel	+ 2
Japan	+ 9
Korea	+ 9
Kuwait	+ 3
Luxembourg	+ 1
Mauritania	0
New Zealand	+ 12
Nicaragua	− 6
Nigeria	+ 1
Norway	+ 1
Pakistan	+ 5
Poland	+ 1
Portugal	+ 1
Rumania	+ 2
South Africa	+ 2
Sweden	+ 1
Switzerland	+ 1
Taiwan	+ 8 (+ 9 in summer)
Turkey	+ 2
USA	− 5 to − 8 (− 4 to − 7 in summer)
USSR	+ 3 to + 13
Vietnam	+ 7
Yugoslavia	+ 1
Zaire	+ 1 to + 2

UTC for different countries. However, most international broadcasters will give the time in UTC.

It is not often that you can identify a station by time, frequency and use of one of the information sources above. You usually need at least one other item of information – say, the language of the broadcast. Signal strength is not really useful as a source of identification information: a strong signal may be received from a fairly distant station, whereas a geographically closer station may give a weaker signal due to propagation conditions.

Language

Although many international broadcasters use English for at least part of their programming, much more enjoyment can be obtained and many more stations identified, if you can recognise a few other languages. Most of us have an idea of how French and German sound, even if we cannot follow what is being said. Learning how other languages sound can be a little difficult, but I have managed to get the 'sound' of several languages by listening to the scheduled programmes in different languages from stations like the BBC *World Service, Voice of America* or *Radio Nederland*. The procedure is simple; find a strong outlet for such a station using the WRTH or another information source, then listen to it and confirm its identification, preferably in English. Then, you should be able to get quite a few languages under your belt. You will probably have to tune to different frequencies to hear languages from different parts of the world, but with a little patience you will soon learn the 'sound' of several languages. Some languages, such as Korean and Japanese, give western ears a bit of difficulty when deciding between them. Other similar sounding languages are Portuguese and Spanish, and some of the Middle Eastern languages.

The WRTH is particularly useful to us when identifying stations that are not transmitting in English. In their station listings, you will find examples of the station identification announcements used in the most common languages used by the station.

The tape recorder can be invaluable when listening to foreign language broadcasts that you are not sure about. Start it running on a broadcast shortly before the half-hour or hour, when a station identification announcement is most likely. Then, even if the announcement was very rapid, you can replay the tape to get a more positive identification.

Armed with these three pieces of information and a frequency list-ing, preferably one giving details of schedules, etc., we can make a tentative identification of the station. Remember to take the *probability* of the station being heard into account as well as the possibility of it being heard! A 1000 watt radio station on an island in the South Pacific is *most* unlikely to be heard in the UK in the middle of the day! Use your knowledge of propagation to make this sort of judgement. Other clues to a station identification include its direction from you; if you have got a beam aerial of any type you can calculate a bearing. What does the programming sound like? Is martial music on a great deal of the time, or political harangues? Is a particular country or name of a person mentioned frequently? If you heard the signal sign off, followed by a tone, can you approximate the pitch of the tone heard? All of these may enable you to narrow down the list of possible suspects to a few or even one. Of course, in some cases you will need confirmation, prefer-ably from a station identification announcement or an interval signal.

Station IDs and interval signals

The station ID, or **id**entification announcement is of course, the most positive way of identifying the station. The announcer literally tells you who you are listening to. Often, at the same time, a list of frequencies in use is given. The ID is given at the start and often at the end of most broadcasts from international broadcasters. On the quarter, half and hour are the most popular times for station IDs to be given, though you may often hear them hidden in the programming. For example, a reporter may be heard to say 'reporting for *Voice of America*'.

The *interval signal* (IS) is a characteristic signal put out by a station before its broadcasts start. It often consists of a phrase of music, drums, birdsong or tones that are broadcast repeatedly until the pro-grammes start. After a while, you get to recognise the more common of these. The WRTH lists many of these ISs, in some cases with the musical notation. I cannot read music, but even *I* can identify some ISs from this! To give a couple of examples, the BBC *World Service* uses *Bow Bells* and the melody *Lilli Bolero*, the *Voice of America* uses *Yankee Doodle* and *Radio Australia* uses *Waltzing Matilda* and the call of the Kookaburra bird.

Simultaneous broadcasts

Many broadcasters transmit signals on several frequencies simultaneously. This allows us to identify a variety of outlets for that station at once or to confirm that we are listening to a particular station by tuning to another frequency on which it should be operating and listening for the broadcast there.

Of course, a station may not be operating on a particular frequency, or the propagation on certain frequencies may not be good enough to get a signal from the station to our receiver. However, if you can listen to two or more outlets at once it can be very useful. For this reason, a second receiver is often quite useful, though you can do this *split frequency* listening on just one receiver with care, especially if your receiver is a modern one with memories which can be programmed to hold the frequencies of interest. You can then go to each frequency in turn, very quickly.

Relay stations

Just because you heard a station identifying itself as *Radio Japan* does not mean that the transmitter broadcasting that station is actually in the land of the rising sun! Many international broadcasters have relay stations in countries nearer to the geographical target area of the broadcasts than is the broadcasters home country. These are called *relay stations*, because they relay the transmissions to a wider audience and at better quality than would otherwise be possible without using very high powers. Typical examples are the presence of *Voice of America* relays in the UK and Greece, and *Radio Moscow* relays in much of Eastern Europe.

Determining where in the world a broadcast originates is not too difficult once you know the station involved *and* you have got a good frequency list. All three books listed earlier indicate the geographical location of transmitters. You will find the odd frequency where two or more outlets are listed in different geographical locations. Finding out which country is originating the broadcast you are hearing is not easy. You can often make a good guess based on your knowledge of propagation (Chapter 13), and on published information. Occasionally, you will hear an *echo* on a signal. This often indicates that there are two transmitters on that frequency carrying the same signal. The echo can be caused by a tiny difference in the time it takes signals from different places in the world to reach our receiver aerial.

Relay stations can be useful in that they allow us to hear stations from countries that might not otherwise be received. An example of this is that *Ascension Island* is quite easy to hear by virtue of a **BBC** *World Service* relay there.

Not listed!

Just occasionally, you will hear a station that you can recognise but that is not listed on that frequency at that time. There are three explanations for this:

1 a change in schedule from that listed in your information. This happens occasionally, though such changes are often broadcast by the station concerned in good time. Sudden changes are occasionally noted; for example, a transmitter on one frequency may break down causing a change in frequency.

2 a brand new station may be on the air.

3 the signal is a spurious one, generated by your receiver; or it could be an accidental station, as discussed later.

Before claiming a new frequency for a particular station, check for image reception and the other sources of accidentals. Recent DX newsletters, DX programmes or magazine DX columns may carry more up-to-date information.

Listening to domestic broadcasters

Much of what was written above about listening to the international broadcast stations applies to listening to the lower-powered domestic broadcast stations. The big difference is that the language used is almost always one of the regional languages of the area and English is seldom encountered unless the signal originates from somewhere like Australia or Canada. In Africa, for example, you will find many stations using French, and in South America a mixture of Portuguese and Spanish will be heard.

Due to the lower power and the frequencies often used by domestic broadcasters (see Chapter 14) the domestic broadcast stations are often buried under interference, either from other broadcast stations or utility stations. A set with good selectivity is thus essential here, and peripheral devices such as a notch filter can be invaluable in getting rid of heterodynes. On the lower frequencies occupied by domestic broadcasters, roughly between 3 and 5.5 MHz, interference is also present from tropical thunderstorms.

Identification of these stations is a little more difficult than with the international broadcasters, due mainly to the lack of frequent ISs and identification announcements. We have to base our identification on frequency, time, propagation and language. Again, a good source of accurate and up-to-date information is essential. I use the WRTH and magazine listings. Additional information can be heard on the DX programmes broadcast by the international stations. Even then, you will find that stations are not always where printed information says they should be!

Additional clues about the likely identity of a station can be obtained from any local time checks given, frequent mention of people or places, and so on. Life is made a little easier for us, though, by the fact that they do not change frequencies to take into account time-of-day, etc (as they are intended for local coverage only). Also, the frequencies mainly used by domestic stations, between 2.5 and 5.5 MHz, are commonly only occupied by one or two stations.

An additional reception problem, on the frequencies between about 2.5 and 3.5 MHz is that of harmonic signals from strong medium wave stations. It is very annoying to spend an hour or two trying to identify a station as a distant domestic broadcast station if it turns out to be the second harmonic of a European medium wave station! These will be covered when we look at accidental transmissions later in this chapter. We will look at the bands used by most domestic broadcast stations, often called the *tropical bands*, in greater detail in Chapter 14.

Suggested introductory listening

Well, after that brief review of international and domestic broadcast stations, it is time to get the receiver turned on for a quick 'world tour' by radio. The stations listed here are reasonably easy to receive on a simple superheterodyne or regenerative set under suitable conditions with a simple longwire aerial. They were received in the summer of 1987, so do remember that schedules and frequencies used may have changed.

HCJB, Ecuador	15270 kHz	2142 UTC
Radio Pakistan	17660 kHz	0800 UTC
Radio Canada International	17875 kHz	2033 UTC

Radio Australia	17715 kHz	0806 UTC
Swiss Radio International	9655 kHz	1018 UTC
Radio Budapest	9835 kHz	2018 UTC
Africa Number 1, Gabon	4830 kHz	2020 UTC
Voice of Free China, Taiwan	9785 kHz	2100 UTC

Listening to amateur stations

Amateur radio stations provide us with some true DX, as well as some very interesting listening. You may hear stations operated from a base in the Antarctic; the chap down the road with the big aerials in the back garden; or a portable station that is run from batteries. Amateurs may operate when they like, but their power and the frequencies they can use are restricted.

These low-powered stations are operated by individuals who have passed an examination and a test of proficiency in sending and receiving morse code. The licence thus obtained allows operation in a variety of frequency bands from 1.8 MHz upwards; some of the amateur bands extend well into the microwave region! The exact frequencies that amateurs are allowed to use will be discussed in Chapter 14, along with the broadcast bands. Like the broadcast bands, the amateur *frequency allocations* are set by international law.

Modes of operation

The broadcast stations that we have mentioned so far almost all operate using amplitude modulation, though there are a couple of experimental SSB broadcasts put out by some international broadcasters. Amplitude modulation of a radio wave is rarely used by amateurs due to its relative inefficiency. After all, amateurs have not got the power that their 'big brothers' have and do not want to waste any of it. So, what other methods of modulation do they use?

CW

We have already seen how we can put information on to a radio wave by interrupting the wave to produce a CW signal. Amateur operators, especially DXers, use CW frequently, due to its ability to penetrate through interference *and* due to the ease with which CW transmitters can be built.

SSB

Single side band is the most common mode of voice communication on the amateur bands between 1.8 and 30 MHz. Its use is forbidden on three of the bands (see Chapter 14), but elsewhere you will hear amateurs from all countries using it. By convention, lower sideband is used on the bands below 10 MHz and upper sideband is used on the bands above 10 MHz.

NBFM

Narrow band frequency modulation is quite widely used on the 10 metre amateur band, mainly for talking with local stations.

RTTY

Radio teletype signals are transmitted by amateurs in most bands. RTTY has experienced a recent upsurge of interest on the amateur bands as operators put their home computers to work at sending and receiving RTTY signals. A baud rate of about 45 bauds has become standard. We will look at the decoding of RTTY signals in Chapter 15 when we look at how the computer can be used in short wave listening.

Other modes

In the HF bands, amateurs also use a method of transmitting static pictures called *slow scan television*. In this mode, pictures are sent between amateurs by coding the picture information as audio tones. These pictures are not of the same quality as broadcast TV pictures, but occupy a narrow bandwidth and require relatively simple equipment with which to decode them. It is possible to use a computer to do this, but we will not go into the subject in this book.

Further specialised transmission modes include *ASCII, AMTOR* and *packet radio*. Apart from a brief explanation of these modes, we are not going to look in to the decoding of them here, as it is rather beyond the scope of the book.

ASCII

Data is transmitted between stations in a similar way to that in which RTTY is sent. However, rather than the 5-bit code used by RTTY, ASCII uses a 7-bit code. It is sent and decoded by computers. The baud rate used is often around 110 baud.

AMTOR

AMTOR (amateur microprocessor-controlled teletype over radio) is a means of sending textual messages over the air waves with a degree of error correction built in, thus cutting down problems with interference which can cause difficulties with both RTTY and ASCII. It operates at about 100 baud, and is based on a commercial system called *SITOR*. AMTOR works in three modes:

1 *mode A*. This is called ARQ (automatic repeat request) and, in it, one station transmits a few characters, then waits for the station at the other end of the link to acknowledge receipt of these characters before sending the next batch. If the acknowledgement does not come, then the first characters are re-transmitted. This is only used when there is *one* station receiving the AMTOR signal; the acknowledgement can only come from one other station.

2 *mode B*. This is known as FEC (forward error correction) mode and in it each block of characters is sent twice in succession. There is no acknowledgement signal to be received and so the AMTOR signal can be received by any number of stations. The chance of error is reduced simply by repeating each letter in the message.

3 *mode L*. This is used by stations which are simply listening to an AMTOR transmission between two other stations.

Packet radio

This is the last of the digital communication modes, and is fairly recent but is catching on. Packet radio is a technique whereby data is transmitted between stations in the form of bursts called *packets*. Each packet is labelled with a code signifying the identity of the station it is being sent to. As these packets are short, several stations can operate at the same time on one frequency. If a packet is received correctly, an acknowledgement signal is sent to the originator and the next packet is sent. Otherwise, the packet is re-transmitted.

Getting started

Amateur band listening requires a good receiver and a decent aerial system for DX stations to be received. However, you can still have great fun listening to amateurs on very simple equipment, such as regenerative receivers. The main requirement is that the receiver should have some means of resolving single sideband transmissions and CW, such as a beat frequency oscillator or a product detector. In addition, good selectivity is essential, so look for a receiver with switchable selectivity for CW and SSB (Chapter 11).

Details of the amateur bands can be found in Chapter 14, and the best ones to start listening on are the 80 metre (3.5 to 3.8 MHz) and the 20 metre (14.0 to 14.45 MHz) bands. The former will give many UK signals during the day and many signals from further afield at night, whereas the latter will give DX stations, under good conditions, throughout the daylight hours and for a little time after dusk and before dawn. At first hearing, tuning over either of these bands will probably make you wish that you had taken up a simple hobby, like bell-ringing or bee keeping!

There are so many stations! The best approach to listening is to find the strongest SSB signal in the band, and then resolve it using the techniques already discussed. Alternatively, if your CW is up to it, go for strong CW stations. Concentrate on strong stations until you get the feel of the controls of your receiver, be it a state-of-the-art, fully-synthesised, does-everything-but-make-the-tea receiver or a single-transistor regenerative set. The ability to *operate* the set is crucial when listening to the amateur bands. Once you have got the hang of your receiver, *then* go for the weaker stations.

Identifying amateurs

Unlike the broadcast stations, amateurs do not run to a schedule and operate on many different frequencies within their allocated bands; there is no WRTH for amateurs, only call books which indicate where a given amateur lives and his or her callsign.

Each country that has an amateur radio service gives its amateurs a unique *callsign* which that amateur uses when he or she is on the air. This callsign varies in structure from country to country, but always consists of two parts: the *prefix* which indicates the country or area of country from which the amateur hails and; the *suffix* which, in conjunction with the prefix, uniquely identifies the amateur. For example, the letter *G* as the first part of a prefix indicates that the amateur has a UK licence. In some cases, there is a second letter after *G*. If there is a second letter, then this indicates the area of the UK in which the amateur lives:

G	England
GW	Wales

GM	Scotland
GD	Isle of Man
GJ	Jersey
GU	Guernsey
GI	Northern Ireland

A UK callsign then has a number, and this number also indicates something about the status of the amateur; for example, *G7 G1, G6* and most *G8* stations are licenced for operation on the amateur frequencies above 50 MHz. On the other hand, *G0, G2, G3* and *G4* stations can all operate on any amateur band, these operators having passed a test in morse code. *G0* stations are the more recently licensed stations, and *G2s* are the 'old guard'.

There then follows a three letter suffix, which is allocated sequentially and acts as an identifier for the amateur. Within each block of callsigns allocated to a given number these three letters will not be repeated. So, you might hear *G3ABC* and *G4ABC* on the bands, but you will not hear a *GM3ABC* at the same time. There are a few amateurs who possess callsigns with only two letters after the number; all these stations were licensed before the second world war, and are licensed for operation on all amateur bands, even if they are *G8* stations. Some three letter groups, which might be confused with Q code signals (see later) are not allocated. In addition, you may also hear stations sporting callsigns beginning with *GB*. These are special-purpose stations, set up for some particular special event or for an experimental reason.

Other countries have other prefix letters; *W* and *K*, for example, indicate American stations. Also, foreign countries use their prefix letters and numbers to indicate geographical regions as well as or instead of licence class. These geographical areas to which a certain prefix refers are called *call areas.* You will occasionally here a callsign followed by the words *mobile, portable* or *alternative.* These indicate that the station is not at its usual place.

Mobile indicates that the station is being operated from a vehicle of some sort. The phrases marine mobile or maritime mobile indicate that the station is being operated from a sea-going vessel. You will see such callsigns written as *GOZZZ/M* or *GOZZZ/MM.*

Portable indicates that the equipment is being operated from a site free of mains power. The station is driven or carried to the spot and then set-up and powered by batteries or a generator. For example, *GOZZZ/P.*

Alternative indicates that the station is being operated from a fixed site (the usual definition is an address to which post can be delivered) that is not the usual home of the operator. For example, *GOZZZ/A*.

You will find that amateurs give their call signs frequently on air. In fact, they have to do so, by the regulations concerning amateur radio. You may well hear something like:

WZ1ZZZ from *GOZZZ*
WZ1ZZZ, this is *GOZZZ*

In both cases, *GOZZZ* is the station just finishing transmitting and *WZ1ZZ* is the station with whom GOZZZ is in contact. The transmitting station usually gives his or her callsign last, and quite often mentions the station that they are talking to. You might not, of course, be able to hear both ends of a particular conversation. If an amateur talks for a very long time, you may hear him slip his callsign in partway through the conversation; in the UK, amateurs have to give their callsign at least once every 15 minutes. At the same time of writing, some alterations were being made to the Amateur Radio Licence.

Sources of information

There are a couple of useful books and magazines to have around when listening on the amateur bands. The *Amateur Radio Operating Manual*, edited by R. J. Eckersley and published by the *Radio Society of Great Britain* (RSGB) gives a wealth of information on amateur operating methods and also contains a list of current prefixes. A couple of the magazines listed in the broadcast band section, earlier in this chapter, also carry amateur radio information. *Radio Communication* is the magazine of the RSGB and is obtainable when you join the society, a course of action that I would advise anyone interested in amateur radio to take. It contains constructional information and lots of news as to what is happening in the world of amateur radio. Various DX clubs also publish prefix lists regularly, because there are occasional changes to the prefixes in use by a country. A second interesting book is *A Guide to Amateur Radio* by Pat Hawker, also published by the RSGB. For both RSGB books, do try and get the latest edition.

Amateur operations

Amateur speech contacts can be a little bewildering until you get the hang of things. This is due mainly to the jargon and abbreviations used by amateurs. Let us look at some of what you may hear.

CQ is an abbreviation of 'seek you'. It is used by amateurs as a general call, indicating that they are waiting for a contact. You may hear a CQ call aimed at a particular country, such as 'CQ Australia', which indicates that the amateur is particularly interested in getting a reply from that continent. The prefix for a country is often used instead of the name of the country in CQ calls. Also commonly heard is 'CQ DX' where a station is looking for a distant station with which to make contact. A typical CQ call might be:

CQ CQ CQ from GOZZZ

A station might reply to such a call with something like:

GOZZZ GOZZZ this is WZ1ZZZ calling

and a contact is thus established.

Q-code. In the early years of radio, when virtually all communication was via morse code, a set of internationally recognised abbreviations was established to help speed communications. These were three letter groups, beginning with the letter Q, hence it was called the Q-code. It is still in use today, in both amateur circles and commercially. Although intended for CW use, it is also used in speech contacts. A Q-code abbreviation can be a statement or a question, depending upon how it is used. For example, 'QRM?' would mean 'Is there interference?' A list of the more common Q-codes is given in Table 12.2.

Phonetic spelling. A short period of listening will soon reveal stations saying something like:

CQ CQ CQ from Golf Zero Zulu Zulu Zulu

especially if the signal is weak. This amateur is using the phonetic alphabet. Letters are spelt out by using words that are easily recognisable as beginning with that letter. The accepted version of the phonetic alphabet is shown in Table 12.3. It is used whenever there is a chance of the receiving station making an error in spelling, such as in names of people or places. Although there is an accepted version of the alphabet, you will find many variations of it on the bands.

Rubber stamp contacts. This is a contact between two stations which is very rapid, stations exchanging the bare minimum of information such as call signs, location and reports on each others signal quality. These are particularly common if one station is a DX station; clearly, others will want to contact, or *work* him. They are also common in contests, where amateurs vie with each other to amass points based on stations and countries contacted in a set period of time.

Rag chewing. This type of contact is more like a normal conversation, and is often found on the 40 and 80 metre bands between local

Table 12.2 Q-code abbreviations as used by amateurs.

Amateurs use Q-code signals in a slightly different way to that in which they are used by commercial stations. Here are the amateur codes.

QRG   What is my exact frequency?
       Your exact frequency is ...
QRK   What is the readability of my signals?
       Your readability is ... (1–5), see RST code
QRM   Is my signal interfered with?
       Interference is ... (1–5), see SINPO code
QRN   Is there noise?
       Noise level is ... (1–5), see SINPO code
QRO   High power
QRP   Low power
QRQ   Shall I send more quickly?
       Send at ... words per minute
QRS   Shall I send more slowly?
       Send at ... words per minute
QRT   Closing down
QSA   What is my strength?
       Your strength is ... (1–5), see SINPO code
QSB   Fading
QSO   Contact
QSL   Acknowledgement
QSY   Shall I change frequency?
       Change to ... (frequency)
QTH   What is your location?
       My location is ...

When used as a question, you will often hear the signal sent as, for example, 'QTH?' or 'What is your QTH?'. When used as a statement, or a reply to a question, you will hear, for example, 'QTH Sheffield' or 'QRN 5'

Table 12.3 Phonetic alphabet

This is the 'official' version of the phonetic alphabet, though variations on it do exist.

A	Alpha	N	November
B	Bravo	O	Oscar
C	Charlie	P	Papa
D	Delta	Q	Quebec
E	Echo	R	Romeo
F	Foxtrot	S	Sierra
G	Golf	T	Tango
H	Hotel	U	Uniform
I	India	V	Victor
J	Juliet	W	Whisky
K	Kilo	X	X-Ray
L	Lima	Y	Yankee
M	Mike	Z	Zulu

amateurs. They are fairly long and often interesting conversations about technical matters, gardening or whatever else interests the amateurs concerned!

Nets. A net is a group of three or more amateurs occupying the same frequency and conducting a multi-way conversation. Due to the complexities of organising such a net so that each person gets a chance to speak in turn, there are few nets with more than 10 stations active at once.

QRP. This Q-code abbreviation has special significance due to the number of amateur operators, particularly those using CW, who use very low powers for their transmissions. Stations may use only a few watts or even milliwatts to get contacts! QRP stations are cheap to assemble, and are often home built; *real* amateur radio!

Set listening periods (SLPs). These are occasionally arranged by societies or magazines, and listeners are asked to listen to particular bands between particular times and log what they hear. If done over a few hours and with many listeners involved, SLPs can give a very good 'snapshot' of a band at a particular time.

Morse code

Many people wonder why this code is still in use, now we have got satellites and transmission methods like AMTOR or RTTY. Well, it is simply a very efficient and cheap way of getting a message from point A to point B, no matter what the conditions are. CW signals will often be heard well enough to read, where a SSB signal would be totally inaudible. In addition, people who know little of each other's language can easily converse in morse by virtue of the fact that most CW contacts use internationally recognised abbreviations in order to save operator time in transmitting the full words (Table 12.4). Of course, there *is* the problem of learning morse code well enough to read the amateur signals! This is not too difficult, though. Let us have a look at how you might do this.

To start with, Table 12.3 shows the international morse code. This has changed only little since Samuel Morse first invented it. The most important thing to remember is that you must think of the letters as being made up of *dits* and *dahs*, not dots and dashes. A *dah* is the approximate sound that a dash makes, and a *dit* is the sound that a dot makes. A *dah* is three times longer than a *dit*. Thus, the letter *S* is sounded as *di-di-dit*. The letter *A* is *di-dah* and so on. The space between *dits* and *dahs* making up single letters should be a silence equal in length to a single *dit*. Between letters in a word, it is the length of a *dah*. Between words it is the length of 7 *dits*. Learning morse is a matter of learning to receive morse at a good speed; once you can receive, you will find that sending morse, using a practice oscillator like that shown in Chapter 10, requires only a little practice.

Morse speed is measured in *words per minute*. Of course, words vary in length, and so the standard word length used when measuring morse speed is of 5 letters. In fact, the word *PARIS* is used as a standard word for these purposes. In the UK, a proficiency of 12 words of morse per minute is required to get a full licence to allow you to operate on the amateur bands between 1.8 and 30 MHz. On the amateur bands, you will hear a variety of speeds used, from very fast to very slow. Some amateurs give their time freely to produce *slow morse* transmissions that are designed to help people learn morse.

Learning the code

There are a variety of ways in which you can learn the morse code; records are available, along with electronic devices that generate random morse code characters. Alternatively, computer programs can be used; in fact, there is a program in Chapter 15 to help with this.

Table 12.4 International morse code

A	.—	S	...
B	—...	T	—
C	—.—.	U	..—
D	—..	V	...—
E	.	W	.——
F	..—.	X	—..—
G	——.	Y	—.——
H	....	Z	——..
I	..	1	.————
J	.———	2	..———
K	—.—	3	...——
L	.—..	4	....—
M	——	5	.....
N	—.	6	—....
O	———	7	——...
P	.——.	8	———..
Q	——.—	9	————.
R	.—.	0	—————

ERROR		....
AR	(message end)	.—.—.
KA	(start signal)	—.—.—
?		..——..
.		.—.—.—
,		——..——

However, the first thing is to learn the alphabet, including the numbers and punctuation, in morse. Although punctuation does not turn up in the morse test should you take it, you will probably hear it on the air so it is useful for you to know.

There are two approaches to learning the characters:

1 learning the code a few letters at a time, depending upon the alphabet position. That is, say, A to E, then F to J, and so on.

2 learning by the *dits* and *dahs* within a character automatically groups together characters in the following ways;

Group 1 all *dits* – E, H, I, S

Group 2 all *dahs* – T, M, O
Group 3 *di-dah* or *dah-dit* – A, N
Group 4 3 element letters – D, G, K, R, U, W
Group 5 4 element letters – B, C, F, J, L, P, Q, V, X, Y, Z
Group 6 numbers 1 to 5
Group 7 numbers 6 to 0
Group 8 punctuation.

Memorizing the code is not too difficult; you can practice by converting any piece of text, car number plates, notices on buses, etc. into code. Do not worry about getting translation done quickly, just get it right.

Once the code has been memorised, the hard graft starts! This is simply the task of programming your brain to produce the correct letter, number or punctuation character when the sounds representing it are heard *without thinking about it!* You also must get your speed up to a good rate. This is where the various aids to learning morse come in useful. If a friend is also learning morse, this can be quite useful as you can practice together. At this time, when you are trying to get your receiving speed up to a good rate, ignore transmitting, and practice receiving morse for about 30 minutes a day at least. Try reading callsigns, etc. from amateur stations who are slow enough for you to read, or use morse generators, etc.

Write the morse down as you receive it; I use lower case letters, because it is quicker to write an *e* than an *E*. If you miss a letter, just leave a space and carry on. Do not puzzle over the letter, because as you do so you will miss more! Similarily, do not try and predict what letter is coming next; having heard *th* you might expect an *e* to follow; it could be an *o* (those), an *i* (this) or an *a* (that). If the letter following is not what you expect then this will throw you and cause you to lose letters.

Your morse speed will go up in fits and starts; you will probably achieve a certain speed and then stay there for some time before getting any significant increase. A common 'problem' speed is around 8 words per minute; some people get this far and cannot get any higher for a while. Persevere, though; it *will* increase with practice. Try and achieve a speed of around 13–14 words per minute; this should allow you to read almost all CW contacts you will find on the bands and give you preparation for the morse test, should you ever take it.

Transmitting morse is fairly easy once your receiving speed is reasonable; in fact, its quite easy to transmit morse at a speed that is faster than your ability to receive!

Chapter 11 covered the way to use your receiver to get the best reception of morse code transmissions. Once you have copied a few, you will find more abbreviations in use. These are simply to increase the speed at which operators can send messages. For example, the abbreviation *DE*, for the word *from*, is coded as:

dah-di-dit dit

whereas the word *from* would be:

di-di-dah-dit di-dah-dit dah-dah-dah dah-dah

As you can see, it is quite a saving in time. Abbreviations like this also makes CW more useful between people who do not understand a word of each others' languages, because the abbreviations are internationally recognised by amateurs. Table 12.5 shows the more common CW abbreviations. As you listen to amateur broadcasts, you will soon pick up more of the jargon and begin to develop the ability to copy the fainter, more rare stations.

DXing the amateurs allows us to increase the number of countries that we have heard, by virtue of the fact that amateurs occasionally take part in *DXpeditions*: when a group of amateurs take their equipment to a particular part of the world not often heard on the amateur bands (and often not heard on the broadcast band, either!) and *activate* that location for a short time. Listening on the frequencies used by such groups can easily increase your number of prefixes heard, because many countries will be trying to get in touch with the rare station. This occasionally leads to a situation called a *pile up*, which is as unpleasant for the listener as it sounds; dozens of powerful amateur stations causing maximum interference to each other as they all call at once. Apart from causing interference to others, the DX station probably will not hear them, anyway. Pile ups can, however, announce to the listener that a station of interest might be in the middle of it, so once you have become experienced you may be able to listen through the interference and 'bag' a new and rare station.

Beacons

In some amateur bands, you will find transmitters whose sole role in life is to transmit a continuous signal to give users of the band an idea

Table 12.5 Some CW abbreviations

ABT	about
BK	break – indicates that a station wants to interrupt a QSO
CQ	general call to all stations
DE	from
ES	and
FER	for
FREQ	frequency
GD	good
GM	good morning (GE = good evening, GA = good afternoon)
GUD	good
HI	laughter
K	invites other stations to transmit
MSG	message
OM	old man
PSE	please
RIG	transceiver
RX	receiver
TKS	thanks
TX	transmitter
YL	young lady (female operator)
XYL	wife
73	all the best
88	love and kisses

of what conditions are like. These beacons are useful for research purposes, as many amateurs are interested in propagation of radio waves, and the amateur service has contributed a considerable amount to the understanding of how radio waves travel. A couple of beacon frequencies are listed here. They transmit on CW, so you will need a little knowledge of morse to decode them, but they are really very easy to recognise, even for people with little or no knowledge of morse code. The beacons do not operate continuously.

4U1UN/B	14100 kHz	New York
4X6TU/B	14100 kHz	Tel Aviv
GB3SX	28200 kHz	Crowborough, UK
VK6RWA	28264 kHz	Perth, Australia

A comprehensive list of these beacons appears in the *RSGB Amateur Radio Call Book*. This book also lists the callsigns and locations of all licensed amateurs in the UK. Similar volumes are available which cover different countries and even the whole world!

Time and frequency standard stations

The last category of stations that I am going to look at in any detail are the stations that act as frequency and time standards. I will briefly look at accidental stations when we look at interference, but the other categories of stations: utility; personal radio services; pirate and clandestine stations, I will not cover in this book. This is partially due to British law and partially due to the fact that the average listener could find them quite boring!

Why bother with stations that transmit just time information, even if they are very accurate? Well, all the stations in this category use very accurately defined frequencies that vary by infinitesimally small amounts over the years; so they provide us with a means of seeing how accurate the calibration of the receiver is, as well as allowing us to set our clocks! Some of these stations also transmit information useful to us when studying radio wave propagation. So, let us look at a few of these stations.

Where are they?

Many advanced countries in the world have them, though some, like Australia, are (at the time of writing) reviewing whether they should continue to support the stations or not. Whether this move will catch on with other governments is uncertain, but if it does we could lose a useful facility. In terms of frequency, these stations operate around 2.5, 5, 10, 15 and 20 MHz. Some other frequencies, such as 25 MHz, are also used, and you may find some standard frequency stations on rather odd frequencies such as 14670 kHz, a frequency used by the Canadian time station, *CHU*.

What will I hear?

At the risk of making a very bad pun, you might get the 'pip' while listening to these stations! The information on time, etc. that is carried by these stations is in the form of audio tones, morse code, pulses or occasionally SSB transmissions, depending upon the station involved.

The pulse-coded information is often suitable for decoding by computer. Some of the stations operate continuously, whilst others have periods of operation throughout the day. Schedules of operation for these stations can be found in the WRTH.

The following information can be obtained from these transmissions, though not all stations carry similar information.

Time

As stations are often relaying information from the time standards for that particular country, you can at least set your watch by them! On a more serious note, listeners interested in propagation experiments often record radio signals on twin track stereo tape recorders; one track carries the signal in which they are interested and the other the signal from a strong time standard station to give an accurate time recording on tape. The format in which the time is transmitted varies from station to station.

Voice

Some stations, such as *WWV* in the United States and *JJY* in Japan, give time information by AM or SSB voice signals.

Morse

Morse transmission of time is also common. Most people can get sufficient knowledge of morse to copy these signals.

Pulses

Many stations transmit their time information as a series of pulses. For example, the simplest type of pulse encoded time information is where a station transmits a series of second pulses followed by a longer minute pulse. Thus seconds and minutes are easily read off of air, though you need to know *which* minute you are dealing with! More complicated coding systems involve information being transmitted in a computer-readable form called BCD (binary coded decimal).

Weather and propagation information

WWV in the US and *JJY* in Japan are two stations that transmit information useful for predicting how propagation will change in the next few hours or days. *WWV*, for example, transmits details of solar activity and geomagnetic activity (activity of the earth's magnetic field) and these pieces of information can be used to assemble a picture of propagation conditions. We will take a closer look at propagation prediction in Chapter 13. *WWV* also transmits local weather information.

Even if the signal that you are listening to does not carry such information, the reception of the time and frequency standard stations from different parts of the world can give you an indication of whether or you will be able to receive more interesting signals on the amateur and broadcast bands from that part of the world. For example, reception of *WWV* on 15 MHz will indicate that it could be a good time to listen for US amateurs on the 20 metre amateur band, or American broadcast stations in the 19 metre broadcast band.

And, if you build any of the receivers shown in the first part of this book, the presence of these stations can help you calibrate your set.

Listed below are a few time and frequency standard stations that you might like to listen out for. A more detailed list, including details of when stations are on the air, can be found in the WRTH or in the *Guide to Broadcasting Stations* (frequencies only). Please note that reception of *WWV* needs a decent aerial system and a good receiver.

WWV	10000 kHz	continuous
RWM, Moscow	14996 kHz	continous
MSF, UK	60 kHz	continuous

Log keeping

The SWL's log book is simply the record of all the stations that have been heard. It is with great shame that I admit to having lost my first log book which I began when I was 11 years old. Ah well . . .

You may wonder why we want to spend part of the time allocated to radio listening actually writing down what was heard. Well, it is nice to look back on later, it can be useful if we want to get a QSL card from a radio station (see later) and it can be valuable to us in helping us make rough and ready predictions about propagation. After a few months of listening and logging what you hear, you will soon be able to use your log as an extra source of reference when listening.

Questions like 'When did I last hear Australia, and on what frequency?', or 'What countries am I likely to hear at 1500 hours on the 19 metre broadcast band?' can all be answered by a quick look back through the log. In addition, you may hear stations at times when they simply should not be audible on a particular frequency. Keeping a record of these odd reception conditions might one day make a contribution to our understanding of radio signal propagation.

What form does a log take?

If you have an amateur transmitting station, there are some quite precise rules and regulations about what form a log book should take and what information should be stored in there. For listeners, there are no such regulations. Let us start by looking at what we can use as a logbook.

I have used loose leaf files, spiral bound notebooks and hardbound books of the sort used for office record-keeping as log books and have found them all quite useful. You can also get pre-printed log books.

Loose leaf files

A loose leaf file and a couple of hundred sheets of lined A4 paper to go in it make a very nice logbook indeed, though when open it can take up a great deal of space on your desk! Another problem is that you can easily overload the file, resulting in the file opening itself up and dropping all your pages out! However, the file is hard wearing and durable and has the added advantage that pre-printed sheets can be obtained to put in the file. Alternatively, you can use a computer program, such as that shown in Chapter 15, to print out blank log pages for punching and using with a loose leaf file.

Spiral bound notebooks

A4 spiral bound notebooks are very useful in that they can be bent back on themselves on your operating table to take up less space. As they are normally soft-covered, they are not as durable as loose leaf files.

Hard cover books

Stationers will often stock hardback books in a variety of sizes and styles meant for use in offices as ledgers, record books, etc. I tend to use this sort of book for both my transmitting and SWL log. They have the advantage that you can often get books that are already ruled vertically into a few columns. This cuts down the work you have to do to prepare the log for use.

Readymade logs
The RSGB produce a log for SWLs interested in receiving amateurs, and other organisations and individuals produce pre-printed log sheets for use in loose leaf files. However, these are more expensive than the do it yourself approach!

Using a computer
In Chapter 15 we will see how a computer can be used to help us with logging. However, I do not think that a computer program is a replacement for a written log.

Date	Time	Frequency	Mode	Station and remarks	SINPO OR RST
30/5/87	2209	14124	USB	G0CEW	57
30/5/87	2213	15084	AM	IRIB, Iran	44332
30/5/87	2217	15160	AM	Radio Australia	24232
30/5/87	2228	15300	AM	WCSN	44333

Figure 12.1

What to put in the log

Whatever you like! There are many different formats used by listeners for storing information, often in the form of columns across the page (Figure 12.1). As you can see, the usual minimum information put in to the log is date, time, frequency, mode of transmission (AM, USB, CW, etc.) station, remarks and report. You could, of course, arrange the information in a different form to suit your own needs. You might also like to add other pieces of information, such as a column to indicate the equipment you used to receive the station. For example, in my shack I use the letter R to indicate reception on a regenerative receiver, D for direct conversion, G for my Grundig Sattelit 1400 receiver, and so on.

When listening, you do not need to log *all* the stations you hear *every* time you hear them. After a while you will get to know all the really strong signals in a given band and you will be more interested in logging the ones you have not heard before or stations that are interesting for any reason, for example, a normally strong station may be putting out a weak signal. Filling in the log need not be a great exercise in book-keeping. It usually takes me no more than a couple of minutes per station, though if I intend writing to the station to report on their signal then my log book entry can be quite detailed, in order to give the station as much useful information as possible. The information put in each column of a log entry is fairly straightforward.

Date
I usually enter the date as, for example, 26/7/87 for 26th July, 1987. This simply saves time when writing.

Time
Standardise your log time as UTC. So, any time featured in your log should be UTC and not local time.

Frequency
I enter the frequency on which a station was heard, as accurately as possible, in kilohertz.

Station and remarks
Wherever possible, I first enter the station name followed by its geographical location. For exampl ee, a typical entry might read 'BBC *World Service, Ascension Island*'. This indicates that the programme was being relayed by the transmitter on Ascension Island. The geographical location of transmitters radiating signals can be found in the WRTH and some of the other sources of information listed. Some countries, such as the USSR and the People's Republic of China, are not very forthcoming about the exact location of some of their stations, so we often end up putting 'USSR' or 'China' in place of a more detailed location.

Even if I cannot identify the station, I make notes in this column about what I heard, and put a question mark instead of a station name. If I am 90% certain of a station's identity, but cannot hear an announcement of any kind, then I put a question mark in brackets after the name of the station. This reminds me to take another look at this frequency on another occasion.

What goes into the remarks column is purely up to you. If you might QSL the station at a later date (see later), then details of programmes heard should be mentioned as well as technical comments. We will look at this aspect of log keeping when we look at QSL card collecting. As a minimum remarks column entry I make notes of the language used, and possibly program details if of interest. In addition, I make some notes about the technical quality of the signal heard; distortion on the signal, frequency of fading, and so on.

If you are listening to amateurs, you might like to put down the power of the amateur transmission; this sort of information is often mentioned over the air, along with other equipment details. I also like to make a note of the station with whom the amateur is communicating. The other person's callsign will get mentioned occasionally and it is often interesting to see which parts of the world were active at a particular time. Of course, hearing one amateur mention another one's callsign does not necessarily mean that you have logged the second station!

Signal report
This is the technical part of the log entry, but may be really valuable at a later date in that it allows you to try and quantify the overall quality of a radio signal. I often make comments on the technical nature of a signal in the remarks column, usually to expand on what I put in the signal report column. The usual ways of reporting signal quality is as a series of numbers, each number representing some aspect of a signal, such as strength, readability, etc. Here I will look at the three codes commonly used by SWLs for logging broadcast stations and amateurs.

SINPO

The *SINPO* code is used for broadcast stations, and the name stands for **s**ignal, **i**nterference, **n**oise, **p**ropagation **d**isturbance and **o**verall quality. A varient is *SINFO*, where the number for propagation disturbance is replaced by a number for fading. When assembling a signal report, each letter is replaced by a number in the range 1 to 5 to indicate quality.

The big problem with SINPO and any of the other codes, of course, is that they are *subjective*. That is, the report given to a station by one listener may be different to that given by another listener *even if the signals heard coming from the loudspeaker of the receiver were identical!*

For this reason, all of these reporting codes are most useful for allowing a listener to compare signals heard on different occasions on his or her receiver with each other. However, they can give some useful indication of signal quality to radio stations, amateurs, etc. and for this reason we often quote one of the codes when we are writing to a station for a QSL card (see later). Let us look at each of the five numbers of a SINPO report in turn.

Strength

In the SINPO code, the five-point scale indicating signal strength is based upon that used in the Q-code (QSA). This was originally intended for use by commercial radio stations, but is useful for us as well. The five audibility levels are:

1 scarcely audible
2 weak
3 fairly good
4 good
5 very good

In practice, there are no real S5 stations on the bands, with the exception of transmitters that are *very* close by. For this reason, the highest rating I tend to give to a signal is *4*. A similar line of reasoning is applied to levels *1* and *2*; I cannot tell the difference between something that is scarcely audible and weak, so I tend to give a *2* as my lowest rating. I thus have to decide whether a signal is weak, fair or good, which is a lot easier than having to decide between five options and is probably just as accurate, considering these estimations of signal strength are subjective anyway.

In Chapter 11 we saw how S-meters were incorporated into many sets, and we saw that differences between S-meters may occur. For example, some S-meter needles may not even move from the *1* mark even for a very good signal that is totally audible! I use my S-meter mainly as a guide when I am not too sure. It is useful to compare two stations using the S-meter, but I do not put too much faith in them. There are some good meters around, but usually on very expensive sets!

Interference

Interference is best defined as the degradation of a radio signal by another, *man-made* signal on the same or a nearby frequency. There are a variety of sources of interference to signals, some of which we will discuss at the end of this chapter. The difference between interference and noise is that noise is *natural* in origin, as we will soon see. Interfering signals can be in any of the transmission modes mentioned previously. Interference is on a five-point scale as well:

1 extremely severe
2 severe
3 fair
4 slight
5 none whatsoever.

Interference of a value *1* needs a little attention; how do we know that the signal we are interested in is still there, if interfering signals are totally overwhelming it? Well, I very rarely use *1* in my reports for this reason. Occasionally, if I have been listening to a station for a long time and it suddenly is overwhelmed by another station I might enter a *1* in the report for that particular time. Usually, however, the lowest interference report I give is *2*. Reports of *5* are only likely to be obtained on nearby stations – to hear what a *5* sounds like, tune to a local, strong FM station. I base my report on what the signal is like after I have done all I can to clean it up; that is, after making use of things like notch filters, variable receiver bandwidth, etc. You might like to make a report on what it is like *before* you start cleaning the signal up, as well, then compare the two. You should see some improvement! I often make comments in the remarks column about the source of interference if it is recognisable.

Noise
Noise is a signal that causes degradation of the desired signal but which is generated by natural causes rather than by other radio transmitters etc. On occasion, it is difficult to tell the difference between noise and interference. On the lower frequency bands, noise is terrestrial in origin, being caused by thunderstorms and other natural atmospheric electrical activity, such as electrically charged rain drops! Just as radio signals from transmitters are bounced around the world by the ionosphere, these natural signals are also propagated over long distances. As we go higher in frequency, into the 15–30 MHz range, some of the noise we hear, especially on the higher frequencies with good receivers, comes from the sun or outer space. Indeed, the science of radio astronomy has its foundations in work done by an RCA radio engineer,

Karl Jansky, trying to find the causes of radio noise on commercial communications links. He deduced that some of the noise on the high frequency bands was coming from the Milky Way, far out in space. Further work by Grote Reber, a radio amateur, found other sources of radio waves from space, including the sun and the planet Jupiter. You will often hear this noise from space described as *galactic noise*, irrespective of whether it comes from the galaxy or our solar system.

Also, remember that any electrical circuit, such as the front end of our receiver, also generates some noise which is indistinguishable from this external noise.

Noise is on a five-point scale, the same as interference. Again, a local, strong FM signal should give a good example of a noise 5 signal.

Propagation disturbance

Changed to fading in SINFO, propagation disturbance is simply a measure of fading and other problems associated with the propagation of the radio signal from the transmitter to the receiver. The report is based on the following points:

1 *Fade rate.* You can estimate the number of fades in a given period of time, say one minute, from listening to the signal or observing its strength on your S-meter, which is great for this comparative work.

2 *Fade depth.* This is a measure of how great the variation in signal strength is. Deep fades are those in which the signal may actually disappear at the trough of the fading cycle, even though the signal may have been strength 4 at the peak of the cycle. Shallow fades are those in which the strength does not alter all that much. You often find that deep fades are of a fairly low fade rate, and shallow fades are of a faster rate.

3 *Distortion.* As we will soon see, fading can be selective, affecting only one sideband of a broadcast. This can cause distortion.

4 *Other effects.* Other effects can give rise to propagation disturbances. This will be covered in Chapter 13, and include such things as sudden ionospheric disturbances – ionospheric storms.

The propagation disturbance is based on all of these features of the signal, and is again on a five-point scale.

1 severe fading, signal unreadable
2 strong fading, difficult to follow

3 fair

4 very little fading, fades shallow

5 no fading or disturbance

Overall rating

This part of the SINPO report gives a picture of the overall quality of the signal. It should be based upon the other parts of the report, but need not be an average of the other readings. You need to exercise some care here; whilst a SINPO of *22224* is not very likely, you could end up with something like *34342*, if the signal quality sounded muffled, for example. Some writers suggest that you start off by evaluating the overall signal and filling in the overall rating part of the report, then work through the others after deciding *why* you gave that rating.

SIO

SIO is simply an abbreviated form of the SINPO code; SIO stands for: signal, interference, overall, and here the noise and propagation disturbance parts of a SINPO report are combined into the interference part of a SIO report. The reporting scale used for each part of the report is the same as for the SINPO code.

RST

RST is the reporting code used by amateur radio operators. The RS-code is used for reporting on amateur voice or RTTY signals, and an extended form, RST, is used to report on amateur CW signals. The *R* stands for readability, *S* for strength and *T* for tonal quality (of a morse signal).

Readability is measured on a scale of 1 to 5:

1 unreadable

2 difficulty in reading, only some words readable

3 signal readable with some difficulty

4 signal suffering only slight readability problems

5 100% readable

Problems in readability stem from a number of causes. These include receiver problems, transmitter problems, propagation disturbance causing serious fading or distortion or even bad diction by the operator of the transmitter! You very rarely encounter reports of less than 3 on the amateur bands; signals less readable than this and you probably cannot read the call sign of the station!

Signal strength is measured on a 1 to 9 scale, with a few 'extra' points after 9 if you have got a decent quality S-meter on your equipment. The scale is:

1 very faint
2 very weak
3 weak
4 fair
5 moderate
6 good
7 very good
8 strong
9 extremely strong

In addition, you may hear amateurs say that a station is '59 + 20 dB'. This indicates that the received signal is so strong that it exceeds *S9* on the receiver's S-meter. The '20 dB' indicates that it is, by the receiver S-meter, 20 decibels over the *S9* reading. One final point; you will hear amateurs exchanging *59* reports constantly on the air. How many of these signals are actually worth a *59* report we do not really know! So, be as accurate and as honest as possible when noting down these readings.

Tonal quality refers to the quality of a properly tuned CW signal. A rough sounding note to the *dits* and *dahs* merits a *1* or *2*, whereas a pure sound merits an *8* or *9*. If the note is exceptionally stable, you can use the letter *X* in addition to the tonal quality value; this indicates that the signal appears to be so clean that it is coming from a crystal-controlled transmitter. Other letters can also be added, to indicate defects in the signal. Letter *K* indicates that clicks can be heard on the CW when the key is pressed, and *C* (for *chirp*) indicates that the tone of the CW signal changes when the key is opened and closed.

QSL cards and confirmations

In the early days of radio, every station received was a special event for the receiving station concerned; after all, there were not that many transmitters on the air in the first place! There thus grew up a new facet of the hobby of short wave listening; collecting *confirmation cards* (more commonly called QSL cards) from the transmitting station.

QSL is the Q-code signal for 'Please confirm that you received my signal' or 'I confirm that I received your signal'. A QSL is a document of some type, sent by the station concerned, that indicates that on a particular occasion you did indeed receive their signals. There are three broad types of document that stations send out to listeners who ask for QSLs.

QSL card

Figure 12.2 shows some of the QSL cards that I have received. As you can see, they are all roughly postcard size. Some simply indicate the fact that you received the station, while others have an attractive picture on one side and reception details on the other side.

Figure 12.2

QSL letter

These are also called *verification letters*, and simply detail that you did in fact hear the station on a particular day and frequency.

In both of the above, the card or letter should include words to the effect 'confirming reception of our signals'. You may also find that other details about the station are included, such as power, transmitter location, etc. However, without the 'confirming reception' form of words, it is not really a verification that you did, in fact, receive the signal.

Listener cards

These are cards or letters from a radio station saying, in effect, 'thanks for your interest'. They are not really QSL cards or letters, because they do not contain any information to indicate that you heard the station. It can be very frustrating to receive one of these cards when you are expecting a proper QSL card!

Reporting to stations

Of course, to receive a QSL card from a radio station you have actually got to write to them with at least one *useful* signal report. Note that I emphasise useful; most international broadcast stations have professional monitoring services keeping an eye on how their signals reach parts of the world, and so when you ask for a QSL from a station they are often only being friendly by replying. So, give them some useful information about their signals and about their programming. The addresses of broadcast stations can be found in the WRTH, which also lists the QSL policy of stations. Most will confirm, though some require return postage to be sent with the report. A few do not confirm at all: often the domestic broadcast stations who are not really concerned if their signals are received overseas.

Amateur stations are a slightly different situation. Some amateurs will confirm SWL reports which tell them something useful. For example, if an amateur in the US has been calling 'CQ Europe' for hours without getting a reply, you might just get a QSL card if you reported his signals. If he had worked a series of European stations, then you probably would not get a QSL card; after all, he knows he can get his signals into Europe because he had been talking to people there! Stations using home-made equipment are often interested in reception reports from SWLs. Amateurs usually exchange cards with other transmitting amateurs with whom they have had contacts and as cards are quite expensive to print, replying to every SWL report too would soon bankrupt many an amateur operator!

What goes in a report?

There are a few essential pieces of information. First, your location. Give your name and address, as well as a reference to the nearest large city or a lattitude and longitude reference. For the UK, cities like London, Birmingham, Manchester and Edinburgh are good reference points when writing to stations abroad. If you are QSLing local radio stations in the UK, for example, your name and address will probably suffice.

Second, give date and time of reception. Write the date out in full, as there are different systems of abbreviating dates used in different parts of the world. Put the time in UTC. It is important that a report to a station should cover at least 20 minutes of time.

Third, the frequency. I give the frequency on which the station was heard in kilohertz, along with the metre band; e.g. 11800 kHz in the 25 metre band.

Next, what equipment was the signal received on. Here I list the receiver used and aerial details. For the receiver, it is often a good idea to detail its circuitry in broad terms e.g. 10 transistor, dual conversion, superheterodyne, or 3 transistor, home-brew, regenerative, and so on.

Then give the station name, and the SINPO or SIO code. If the signal quality varies through the transmission, make a note of the new SINPO and the time. You can also make comments in your report about sources of interference, quality of sound – in fact, anything that might be useful to the staff of the radio station. You should also detail the programmes heard during your period of listening. Get the times of programme changes, titles of programmes, announcers' names, items from news and weather bulletins, times of sign on and sign off, IS and station ID times and so on. You are proving to the station that you *did* hear them.

Finally, give a comment regarding the programme content. More and more international broadcast stations are wanting to hear from *listeners*, not just DXers to whom they are just another station in the log. They are interested in what you think of the programmes that you hear. Be honest, and express your opinions – politely, of course! Today, most international broadcast stations *know* that they are 'hitting' a particular country with their broadcasts, so station staff are often interested in *how well* their programmes are going down with the listener.

Try to listen for at least 20 minutes to give the station an idea of how

222 Short wave listening handbook

their signals behaved with time. If possible, see how signals from the same station are faring on other frequencies used by that station at that time, and add details of these to your report. Or, listen to the same frequency over a few days, and report how the signals fared from day to day.

Report format

If the report is on one frequency for, say, 25 minutes then I can fit the report onto a single sheet of A4 paper, assuming I type it. Do not try to cram too much on to one page, though.

Clear handwriting or typing is essential for reports, as you may be writing to people whose first language is not English. Indeed, for stations in some parts of the world you will have to get your report translated into a different language. Details of how to report to stations in Spanish, for example, which is the principal language used in Central and South America, can be found in *A Guide to Broadcasting Stations*.

The WRTH details the languages in which stations are prepared to accept reports. However, unless your interest is in QSL cards from the domestic broadcast stations of Africa, South America or Asia then English should be fine. The only other special point to make with regard to domestic stations is that the SINPO or SIO codes may not be recognised by people not involved in international broadcasting. In this case, it is a good idea to put your report of the technical quality of the signal into words.

Tape reports

The advent of the cheap cassette tape recorder has led to the situation where many SWLs have one in their shacks for use during listening. In Chapter 10 we discussed connecting them to the receiver and how to use and maintain them. Some SWLs have used the recorder to tape a broadcast from a station. The tape, and a suitable covering letter, can then be sent to the radio station. The taped portion of the broadcast serves two functions; it proves to the transmitting station that you heard their broadcast and it also gives them a chance to actually hear what their signals sound like. The letter should contain your address, details of time, date, receiver and programme comments.

Not all stations are in a position to process tapes, and some require reel-to-reel tape reports rather than those on cassette. In addition, it is unlikely that you will get your tape back. However, here are a few pointers to go by if you wish to submit tape reports to a station.

Acceptability
Ensure that the station will accept tape reports. Check the WRTH or a similar source of information for this.

Tape type
Some stations can accept cassette tape *or* reel-to-reel, others just reel-to-reel. When you record the signal, record it at the standard speed for whatever type of tape that you are using. Use good quality audio tape; for typical reports a running time of at least 15 minutes and preferably longer is required. C60 cassettes will record 30 minutes per side, and are thus quite suitable. Label which side of the tape contains the program recording.

The recording
Using the microphone of the tape recorder to pick up the sound of the broadcast from the receiver loudspeaker is not good enough. Use one of the techniques mentioned in Chapter 10. Carry out some dry runs on your equipment to get the best settings for the recorder *before* using the recorder when DXing. If the recorder has a monitor function by which you can hear the signal as it is recorded on the tape, plug your headphones in to the socket and adjust the receiver controls for the best quality sound. Do not forget that in many receivers the tape recorder output will be taken from the receiver electronics *before* the final audio stages, and so tone controls, and possibly noise blanking circuits, may not have any effect.

The recording should be as faithful a reproduction of what you heard on the air as possible. The station staff will want to hear what their signal sounds like without any additional distortion, wow, flutter or funny noises from your tape recorder!

Return postage
Putting a few stamps from your own country in the envelope when you write to a radio station is not a good way of giving the station return postage. The stamps will be worthless in foreign countries. There are two ways in which you can send return postage to those stations that need it. First *international reply coupons* (IRCs) can be used. These are international stamps, redeemable in most countries for the cost of the

cheapest form of return postage from the country in which they are redeemed to that from which they were sent. You can also redeem them for cash, and they have become a sort of international currency between DXers in different countries. They are available from most post offices, and one IRC is usually all that is needed for return postage. Some countries do not recognise IRCs, however, and in their case you need to try a second approach.

It is occasionally possibly to send *mint stamps*, from the country concerned, to act as return postage for your QSL card. This is a difficult way of doing things, as the problem is one of getting hold of the stamps!

Final points on QSLs

Just because you have sent a report to a station, do not automatically expect a QSL in return. The station is doing you a favour by replying, so do not *demand* QSL cards, but ask for them politely. You may receive other items, such as pennants, programme information, etc as well as your QSL, and many stations run listeners' clubs that you can join. QSL card collecting adds a new facet to the hobby, and also gives you the chance to comment on the programmes you listen to and to help improve on the technical quality of broadcasts by reporting to stations exactly how their signals, finely polished and sounding wonderful when they leave the studio, arrive at their destination – your receiving aerial.

A final source of help for amateur QSLs can be a *QSL bureau*. This is an organisation set up to facilitate the exchange of QSL cards between ratio amateurs. The bureaux act as 'clearing houses' for QSL cards; you send all your cards to one place and the bureau sends you cards sent to the bureau for you by other stations every now and again. The bureaux can be slow, but they are cheap. QSL bureaux do not usually deal with broadcast band QSL requests. The RSGB bureau offers its services to RSGB members, but SWLs are reminded that cards they request via the bureau should be for reports that are *of value* to the amateur whose signal was heard.

Sources of interference

You will not have to do too much listening before you get to know the bane of the listeners life; interference! We have already discussed the difference between noise and interference, so let us now take a look at the different types of interfering signal that you are likely to encounter. The first group are from other broadcasting stations, so let us start by looking at these.

Co-channel interference

These are interfering signals that are on the same frequency as the station that you are trying to listen to. Unfortunately, there is nothing much you can do about these signals; a directional aerial can help if the two stations are in different directions. If the signals are reaching you by different paths, then the propagation on these paths might be different so that one signal (preferably the interfering one!) might fade more than the other, thus allowing one station to be heard in preference to the other. Another alternative is to wait until one or other station closes down or changes frequency.

Adjacent channel interference

In this case, the interference is caused by a station on a nearby frequency, possibly several kilohertz away. Here, the cause is often inadequate receiver selectivity (Chapter 11). The easiest course of action is to cut down the IF bandwidth of the receiver, if possible, or use an audio filter to cut down the bandwidth at the audio output of the receiver. For example, on one of my receivers I can use a 2.7 kHz bandwidth, designed for use with SSB signals, to cut down adjacent channel interference on AM transmissions.

If a weak station is operating in close proximity to a strong station then the AGC can be turned off and the gain of the receiver manually adjusted. This will often improve reception of the weak signal.

Should signals be *very* close together filtering is unlikely to have much effect due to both stations being within the pass band of the filter; that is, the stations are so close together that to cut one of them out would also cut out a substantial portion of the other. In this case, we have got a similar situation to that in co-channel interference.

A similar phenomenon to adjacent channel interference is that of *splatter* where the sidebands of a signal are so strong that they extend for many kilohertz, or even tens of kilohertz, around the frequency on which the station operates. The interference sounds like a series of noisy crackles and thumps, which gradually form a recognisable signal as you tune towards it. On the amateur bands, splatter can be indicative of either a very close amateur transmitter or a very badly adjusted one!

Untunable signals

You may occasionally suffer from signals that form a broad, noisy 'mush' behind signals of interest and that do not change in strength of quality as you tune. These untunable signals are often to be found on the 49 metre and 41 metre broadcast bands in Europe after dark, when many strong signals are to be found. The problem is caused by overloading of the RF stages of the receiver by the strong signals and their effect is to cause the background mush over a wide range of frequencies. A common cause is the ploy of some beginners to tie a long piece of wire to the telescopic aerial of their receiver. Such receiver inputs are designed to handle only the low signals the telescopic aerial offers and so, when confronted by very strong signals from a long wire simply overload. The solution is to decrease the aerial signal reaching the receiver. An RF attenuator is a useful extra to any receiver that is to be used on the mentioned bands, and in Chapter 10 some simple attenuators, suitable for home construction, are discussed. Overloading can also be reduced by using aerial tuner units and preselectors. Overloading afflicts all receiver types, from crystal sets and regenerative receivers to the latest fully synthesised receivers. The diagnosis is simple; disconnect the aerial and replace it with a shorter one or introduce an attenuator into circuit between the aerial and the receiver. If the mush disappears, the problem has been solved. Strong local signals may also appear at an odd place in the band. This too is probably due to overloading: causing cross modulation.

A second cause of an untunable signal, though only in superheterodyne receivers is that of IF breakthrough, when a signal on the IF of the receiver reaches the receiver IF strip and is amplified as if it came from the mixer. This is only really common if you are in a strong signal area for the signal on the IF, or if you are overloading badly.

Jamming

It is a sad fact of life in the late twentieth century that not all countries agree with the doctrine or attitudes of all other countries, as you will gather from listening to the many opposing points of view expressed on short wave broadcast stations. However, some countries try to stop their peoples listening to certain broadcasts by jamming certain frequencies used by other countries who are beaming towards that country. At the time of writing, the situation has eased somewhat as the political situation between East and West has become a little less fraught. However, frequencies used by the US backed *Radio Free Europe* and *Radio Liberty* are still jammed by the Eastern Bloc countries, though jamming of the BBC *World Service* and *Voice of America* has been lifted. It is not just East and West that take part in this electronic battle; in other parts of the world where tension is present, you are likely to find jamming, such as between the Soviet Union and the People's Republic of China.

From the DXers point of view jamming is bad news because it spreads over several adjacent frequencies. It sounds like a roaring, rushing noise. In the early days, recordings of diesel engines running at full speed were often broadcast though, today, electronics has taken over as the source of the jamming broadcast. Occasionally, one country will broadcast over the top of the signal they wish to jam, hoping that the resultant interference will dissuade their people from listening to the broadcast concerned. Use of narrow bandwidth filters and other such devices can help, but not always. The worst band for jamming, in my opinion, is the 16 metre broadcast band, where several frequencies are constantly occupied by the buzzing roar of the jammer. It is a fact of DXing life that we have to get used to, because it is probably going to be around for some time!

Woodpeckers

No, not the feathered type that could demolish your aerial mast! The *woodpecker* was the name given to an odd 'pecking' noise which was heard wandering around the short wave bands in the mid-to-late nineteen seventies. It appeared to follow the MUF (see Chapter 13) and caused considerable annoyance. Eventually, it became apparent that the signals emanated from the Soviet Union, and various weird theories, including mind control and weather control, were propounded in the press. It turned out to be neither of these; the woodpecker is simply part of a long range radar system designed to 'see' over the horizon to detect any incoming aircraft before traditional radar systems could. It thus used the frequencis on which a signal would travel furthest at any one time, and so it changed frequency as propagation effects changed. Today, the woodpecker is less common, though it is likely that both the US and the USSR use such systems.

Electrical interference

We mentioned a little while back that devices such as thermostats, electric motors and car ignitions can all cause interference to our listening. Though it is sometimes difficult to describe them as noise or interfering signals on a SINPO report, the effects are the same; they stop us from hearing signals of interest. Electrical interference comes from two main sources.

Switching circuits

Here, a circuit carrying an electrical current is interrupted and a small spark generated. This will cause a click in the receiver, and can be caused by anything from the door bell to a lightning flash! These signals are strongest at lower frequencies, often being no louder than the background noise above about 15 MHz, unless the source is close by or large currents are involved. The noises caused by this type of interference are crackles, rough harsh buzzes or popping sounds. Many can be reduced by the use of noise limiters or ATUs, though in some cases you may have to take steps to suppress the source of interference.

Suppression of interference

The first step is to determine where it is coming from. Possible sources are thermostat switches, motors, door bells, light switches, etc. A portable transistor radio tuned to a quiet medium wave frequency (500–600 kHz) is useful here. Move around the house with it and find out where the interference is most intense. If the strongest signal appears to come from walls, then the interference could be being spread by the mains wiring of the house, after being introduced into the wiring by an electrical device. Once localised, some steps can be taken to suppress the device by fitting either a commercially available suppression device or using one of the circuits shown in Figure 12.3. Should you decide to build your own suppression filter, the capacitors must be self-healing devices, of Class X 2 type, specifically designed for use under continuous mains conditions. Any RF chokes used should be capable of handling whatever current is drawn by the device being suppressed.

If interference still persists after suppressing devices around the house, a mains filter can be purchased to plug in between the radio receiver and the mains outlet. This protects the receiver from any noisy spikes on the mains as well as suppressing all mains-borne interference

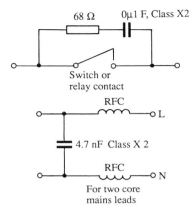

Figure 12.3

at frequences above 100 kHz or so. This can also help suppress noisy harmonics of TV time base circuits (see later).

Some interference can be picked up by the aerial of the set, especially if an indoor aerial is in use. If possible, run the aerial wire as far away from mains wiring as possible. Any persistant buzz on received signals, especially on LF and MF signals, could be caused by your aerial lead running close to a mains wire after entering the house. As well as the mains wiring of the house acting as an aerial and transmitting interference signals, other large metal objects, such as central heating radiators or TV aerial leads can pick up interfering signals and re-transmit them! So, keep your aerial lead away from these objects as well.

Finally, it is as well to remember that some interference comes from outside your home. Nearby small industry, hospitals or neon signs can all generate interference. There are some commercially available suppressors, known as *QRM eliminators* (QRM is the Q-code for interference) which are reported to give good results at reducing such problems, though an ATU will also often help. If severe interference is caused to normal TV and radio reception, then you may be able to get official help in getting the interference suppressed. A booklet, *How to improve television and radio reception* is avaialable from major post offices or the DTI.

Noise from electronic circuits

The commonest problem here is from the time base circuits of television receivers. A circuit operating at 15.625 kHz and producing a saw tooth signal is used to scan the electron beam across the TV tube to form the picture. This causes considerable problems on the long, medium and short waves up to about 15 MHz. Every 15 kHz there is a buzz, and although filters, etc can limit it the only solution is to get the aerial and receiver as far away from TV sets as possible. Some of the interference may travel through the mains supply, so do not run your receiver from a socket on the same part of the house circuit as the TV set, if at all possible. The use of screened co-ax to connect the receiver to the aerial and ATU will also help. Of course, if possible, the best solution is to turn off your own TV; you may still get a little interference from your neighbour's television set, but it will probably be quite faint.

Computers also generate considerable amounts of noise. Other pieces of digital equipment, such as frequency meters, digital clocks and RTTY decoders can all cause interference unless they are properly constructed and screened. More details about curing this type of interference will be given in Chapter 15 when we discuss computers.

Other sources of interference, becoming more and more common, are certain types of telephone equipment provided by British Telecom for either pay phones or office telephone systems. This is a wideband noise which occurs at different points throughout the spectrum from low frequency right through to VHF. Similar problems can be caused by gaming machines or space invader type games in public houses. These sources of interference are difficult to deal with as they are outside your control, and are best treated as electrical interference from outside the house, as detailed above.

Accidental transmissions

Occasionally, interference is experienced from signals that should not be there at all! We have already seen how the superheterodyne and direct conversion receivers and converters can generate spurious signals and how overloading can cause problems. Two other things to consider are: harmonics and ionospheric crossmodulation.

We saw in Chapter 2 how transmitters can generate harmonics, signals that are multiples of the actual frequency being used by the transmitter. These signals are usually filtered out of the signal sent to the aerial. If they *do* reach the aerial, however, they can be radiated like any other transmitted signal and can show up in an unexpected place!

For example, I have heard the third harmonic of a strong station on about 7200 kHz turn up on 21 600 kHz. Harmonics are much easier to isolate if they are out of the normal broadcast bands; if you spot an out of band signal that is not listed as being occupied, is it on a multiple of a broadcast band frequency? If it is, check that frequency and see if the program is being radiated there. If so, you may be hearing a harmonic. Particular problems can be caused by harmonics of medium wave stations falling in the low frequency ranges used by domestic broadcasters. For example, the BBC transmitter on 1215 kHz might be heard as a harmonic on 2430 kHz. Second harmonics are the most common, followed by third harmonics. Fourth and higher harmonics are rare. Indeed, strong harmonics from any broadcast station do not usually persist for long, because the engineering staff are often alerted to their presence and so do something about them!

Ionospheric crossmodulation is covered in greater detail in the next chapter. It can cause interference in areas where strong signals are common. In essence, two radio signals 'meet' in the ionosphere and the stronger one modulates the other, thus producing co-channel interference. The signals do not need to be all that close in frequency, but they must impinge on the same area of the ionosphere. The interference disappears when either signal goes off the air.

THIRTEEN

Propagation

If all radio waves were limited to line-of-sight reception, like TV stations and FM radio, the hobby of SWLing would be very boring indeed! Fortunately for us, not all radio signals behave in this way; radio waves below about 30 MHz can travel, or *propagate*, around the world under the influence of particular layers in the atmosphere.

Reception of distant stations in the MF and HF frequency bands depends upon the *ionosphere*, a region of the atmosphere between 20 and 400 miles above our heads (Figure 13.1). It is a region in which the gases that make up the atmosphere are under heavy bombardment from ultra violet radiation and X-radiation from the sun. These radiations are so strong that the atoms and molecules are ionised – electrons are stripped away from the gases leaving an ionised layer which can bend or absorb radio signals. The number of free electrons – called the *electron density* – depends upon the intensity of the radiation and where in the ionosphere you are looking, because high levels of ionisation occur in specific layers called the D, E, F1 and F2 layers. The greater the radiation is, the more the ionisation, and the level of radiation striking the earth depends upon the time of day, time of year, and the state of the sun. Maximum radiation will occur in winter at local noon, especially when the sun is said to be *active* in radio terms (see later).

In the daytime, all four layers are present, but after sunset the level of ionisation falls, allowing electrons and ionised atoms and molecules to recombine to electrically neutral gas molecules again. This causes the D layer to dissipate, and the F1 and F2 layers to form a single F layer, at a height roughly between the heights of the two daytime layers. All of these layers have different effects on radio signals of different frequencies; for example, the D layer absorbs signals, whilst the E and F layers bend, i.e. refract, radio signals, often bending them

Kilometres

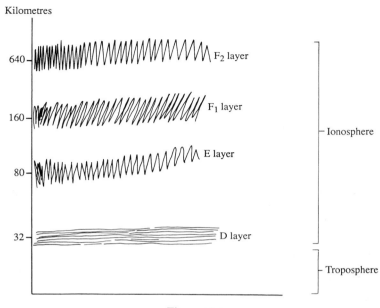

Figure 13.1

enough so as to allow them to return to earth. However, even when the ionosphere is highly ionised, signals above about 30 or 40 MHz usually escape into space unless other forms of propagation, outside the range of this book, take a hand.

Ground and sky waves

When a radio signal is heard in a receiver, the signal will have arrived at the reception site in one of two ways. First, as a *ground wave*, the signal travels along the surface of the earth, or very close to it. Over sea water or very conductive earth, the ground wave coverage for a radio transmitter can be quite good. However, most of the time the ground wave signal fades away with distance. Ground wave propagation is best at VLF and LF, and its range falls rapidly with frequency. MW broadcast transmitters use the effect of ground wave propagation for their daytime coverage.

As a *sky wave*, the radio signal is radiated upwards from the transmitter, out into space. Below 30 or 40 MHz the possibility exists for this

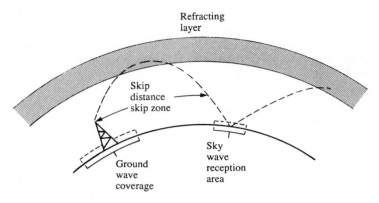

Figure 13.2

sky wave signal to be refracted back to earth by the ionosphere. This will cause the signal to be heard over much greater distances than would be possible if we were to rely totally on ground wave coverage. Long distance radio communication depends upon sky wave propagation.

Between the area served by the ground wave signal from a transmitter, and that served by the sky wave, is an area called the *skip zone* (Figure 13.2). Here, the signal cannot be heard at all. The distance between the transmitter and the start of the sky wave coverage area is called the *skip distance*, and depends upon:

1 the frequency of the signal transmitted.

2 the height of the ionospheric layer responsible for refracting the signal back to earth. The higher the layer is, the longer the skip distance.

3 the angle at which the radio signal strikes the ionospheric layer. If the signal strikes the ionosphere at a fairly shallow angle, then the skip distance will be greater.

As indicated in Figure 13.2, a signal can bounce back to the ionosphere from the skip zone, thus causing another skip zone to occur even further away from the transmitter as the signal is refracted back to earth via the ionosphere. The amount of signal reflected off the ground back to the ionosphere depends upon the conductivity of the ground, sea water giving the best results. A single *ground – ionosphere – ground* path taken by a signal is called a *hop*, and where the signal travels by being refracted by the ionosphere more than once we have *multi-hop* propagation. These multiple hops each rob the signal of some of its strength. Clearly, each hop is longer if the refraction of the signal back to earth is via one of the F layers rather than the E layer, due to the greater height of the F layers.

The role of the ionosphere

At local noon there are likely to be four ionospheric layers above your head – the D, E, F1 and F2. There are no A, B or C layers to worry about; the D layer was named as such just in case lower layers *did* show up, but none have yet!

The D layer

This is only present in daylight and is responsible for absorbing MF and low frequency HF sky wave signals. Thus signals in the MW broadcast band, the 160 m and 80 m amateur bands and the tropical bands are limited to ground wave coverage throughout daylight hours. Signals in the 49 and 41 metre broadcast bands and the 40 m amateur band are also attenuated to some degree, though as the frequency increases the absorption decreases, until by 9 or 10 MHz signals pass straight through the D layer under normal conditions. The D layer never bends signals back to earth.

Particularly dense ionisation of the D layer, as might be caused by storms on the sun, can lead to the absorption of signals throughout the HF bands, with only strong signals above 15 MHz being audible via sky wave reception. Such an incident is called a *sudden ionospheric disturbance* (SID), and is usually short-lived and occurs only in daylight hours.

The E layer

This layer is responsible for long distance propagation on MF and the lower HF bands up to about 10 MHz in daylight hours, assuming the signals can penetrate the D layer. Skip distances of 1000 miles are possible. At night, the D layer vanishes, and the E layer, though diminished in ionisation due to recombination, can still refract the MW and low HF signals, giving ranges of a few thousand miles on a single skip.

The E layer is thus responsible for transatlantic reception of US broadcast stations on the MW band.

The skip distance for the E layer is such that, around dusk, the skip zone and the ground wave coverage area may overlap. This will lead to signals in the overlap zone arriving by two means; one direct, via the ground wave, and the other via the E layer. Because of movements in the ionosphere, the distance travelled by the sky wave will vary slightly with time and this will result in phase differences between the ground and sky wave signals, leading to fading and distortion of the signal.

A particularly intense form of ionisation occasionally occurs in the E layer which is capable of refracting signals back as high in frequency as 144 MHz! This is called *sporadic E*, and will also allow E layer propagation of signals above about 10 MHz. Skip distance is the same as for normal E layer propagation.

The F layer

This is actually two distinctly separate layers in the daytime, F1 and F2, but after dark the ionisation level falls and they merge into a single layer. In daytime, the F2 layer is responsible for propagation above about 10 MHz and the F1 layer for the propagation of signals below about 10 MHz that have passed through the E layer. Because of the differing heights, F1 and F2 skip distances are different; F1 skip being a 1600 km or so, whilst F2 skip is in the 3000 – 4000 km mile range. Multiple hop propagation is also possible via the F layers.

The MUF

The highest frequency refracted back to earth from the ionosphere on a particular path is called the *maximum usable frequency* (MUF). It is dependant upon the time, season, the state of the sunspot cycle, and the angle at which the wave hits the ionosphere. Estimates of MUF at a particular place are obtained by using a special type of radar called an *ionosonde*, which transmits a pulse of radio signal vertically into the ionosphere. The time between transmission and reception of the reflected signal gives a means of calculating the height of the ionized layer responsible for the refraction. The frequency used is gradually increased until no reflected signal is received; the highest frequency that will be refracted back to earth is called the *critical frequency* for that layer, FF_c or FE_c, and the MUF is usually estimated at $3FF_c$ or $5EF_c$.

Although transmissions at MUF would have the greatest range for a given transmission power, they would also be more unreliable, and fading and other disturbance to the signal would occur as the MUF changed. For this reason, broadcast stations will not operate at the MUF, but at a frequency somewhat lower, often called the *optimum traffic frequency*.

In general, the MUF is at its highest around 1100 to 1400 hours, local time, and is higher at sunspot maximum. In addition, the MUF is higher in winter due to increased ionisation, and is usually higher on north/south paths than on east/west paths.

The F layer at night is more effective at propagating frequencies below 10 MHz, as the ionisation level decreases and such signals pass through the E layer. Again, lower frequency propagation via the F layer is better in winter than in summer.

Chordal hop propagation

An interesting type of propagation occurs via the F layer around dawn and dusk, when the F1 and F2 layers are forming or recombining. Signals are propagated between two places both in darkness provided that it is dawn at one end and dusk at the other. As can be seen from Figure 13.3 the signal does not actually make contact with the ground during its travels; this is what makes chordal hop different to normal skip propagation.

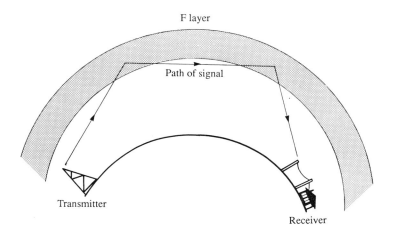

Figure 13.3

Long and short paths

A radio signal will normally travel by the shortest path between transmitter and receiver, the *short path*. For example, the short path between the UK and Australasia is across Asia. However, sometimes it is more likely for signals to be heard via the *long path* route, which for Australasia is across South America and the Pacific Ocean. In terms of bearings, the long path and short path are 180° apart. When it is dawn at one end of the path, and dusk at the other, chordal hop propagation is often responsible for long path reception.

Fading and distortion

The most noticeable effect of all this toing and froing between ground and ionosphere is that the signal we receive is usually subject to fading and even distortion. These two effects are caused by the passage of the signal through the ionosphere.

There are four ways in which fading of a radio signal can occur. The first is simply by the ionosphere absorbing the signal. This is what happens, on an extreme level, during a SID. Fades caused in this way are called absorption fades, and are usually slow to take effect and are long lasting.

The second type of fading occurs when we are within the ground wave coverage area for a station *and* a sky wave reception zone. This is particularly common on MW broadcasts, or the LF amateur bands. Fading here is caused by changes in the phase relationships between the sky wave and the ground wave. As the height of the refracting layer changes, the effective path length of the sky wave changes, thus altering the phase relationship.

Polarization fading is caused by the polarization of the radio signal being twisted by the effects of the earth's magnetic field in the ionosphere. A signal transmitted from a horizontally aligned aerial would be horizontally polarised, and best reception would be obtained using an aerial that was also horizontally polarised. However, this signal can have its polarisation twisted in its axis, through the ionosphere and so the polarisation of the signal received will vary with time.

Finally, there is *skip distance fading*, where a receiving station is on the edge of the skip zone for a given transmitter. As the height and ionisation of the refracting layer changes, the skip distance will also change and so fading of the signal will be noted.

Distortion

Changes in the ionosphere can affect different frequencies by different degrees, as we have already seen. However, some changes will cause fading of some parts of the sidebands of an AM signal and not others! This will lead to distortion of the received signal. SSB is less likely to suffer from this effect.

Solar influences

The sun has further influences on ionospheric radio propagation than just supplying the radiation to cause the ionised layers. Sunspots, relatively cool areas on the sun which have considerable magnetic fields associated with them, have a great effect on the ionosphere. Solar flares, large outbursts of hydrogen gas which emit light, X-rays and UV-radiation as well as charged particles, also affect the propagation of radio signals by causing SIDs. Also associated with SIDs is a phenomenon called *sudden enhancement of atmospherics* (SEAs) where the propagation of radio signals caused, say, by lightning flashes, on frequencies between 20 and 30 kHz is enhanced.

Large numbers of sunspots will cause an increase in the MUF, thus leading to better reception on the higher frequency bands. Low sunspot counts will favour reception on the lower frequency bands. The number of sunspots varies with time. In the short term, the sun rotates on its axis once in every 27 days, and so long-lived sunspots will exert their maximum influence once every 27 days. Over a period of years, the number of sunspots on the sun's surface follows a cycle of 11 years. The last maximum in this cycle was 1978–1981, when phenomenal results on the HF bands above about 17 MHz were experienced. In the minima years, though, bands above about 22 MHz can be totally devoid of signals.

Although this 11 year sunspot cycle exists, there have been periods in the earth's history when there have been prolonged minima, like the *Maunder Minimum* of the 17th century. Also, it is difficult to tell what the highest sunspot count is going to be until it happens, so it is quite difficult to predict the actual month and year at which the peak will occur. However, chances are, the next maximum will be in the period 1990 to 1992.

In addition to these effects caused by the ionising radiations given out by the sun, the sun itself is a powerful source of radio waves, and it is possible to detect these signals on the 10 m amateur band as a rushing noise.

Geomagnetic influence

The earth's magnetic field has an effect on radio propagation particularly when magnetic storms which lead to a deterioration in reception condtions are prevalent. Signals passing through the auroral zones around the poles are particularly prone to effects caused by the earth's magnetic field.

Beacons and propagation indicators

The 20 and 10 m amateur bands contain beacon transmitters in different parts of the world which allow amateurs or listeners interested in propagation to monitor signal strength over a period of time and see changes in propagation patterns. This is one area in which listeners can make a valuable contribution to the science. Details of beacon frequencies can be found in *The Radio Amateur and Listener's Pocket Book* by Steve Money, *G3FZX*, published by Heinemann Professional Publishing.

Useful information regarding propagation can be obtained from the broadcasts of *GB2RS*, the news station of the Radio Society of Great Britain, or the American station *WWV*. The former stations are run by amateurs from their own amateur station, and use a special callsign for news broadcasts. They can be heard on a variety of bands on Sunday mornings. The latter station transmits on 10 MHz, 15 MHz and 20 MHz and broadcasts propagation information at 15 minutes past each hour. The two main pointers to propagation conditions given by these transmissions are solar flux, and the A index.

Solar flux

This is a measure of the radiation from the sun on a particular frequency, and provides a measure of the overall activity of the sun. A reading of below about 70 is said to be quiet, readings over 90 indicate DX possibilities on the higher short wave bands. Readings over 200 indicate that these conditions will persist even after dark – very good conditions indeed. The solar flux roughly follows the 11 year sunspot cycle.

A index

Also called the *geomagnetic A index*, it is a measure of the activity of the earth's magnetic field. The A index is measured on a scale of 0 to 400, and the higher the quoted value the more disturbed is the magnetic field, refering to conditions over a given 24 hour period, and best DX conditions are for low values. High values indicate magnetic storms, which can disturb conditions for a few days at a time, particularly at high lattitudes.

Anomalous propagation

Just occasionally, radio signals are received when they should not be, and the search is on for a form of propagation to explain these anomalies. To finish off this chapter, let us look at a few oddities in propagation.

Ionospheric cross modulation

This is an effect once called the *Luxembourg effect* because it was first noted with regard to broadcasts on powerful transmitters from that country. Two signals, one of which must be powerful, impinge on the same part of the ionosphere. The modulation content of the stronger signal gets superimposed upon the weaker signal, so that anyone listening to the sky wave signal from the weaker station will, also hear the stronger signal. It is basically the same sort of thing that happens when we get cross modulation due to the overloading of the front end of receivers, but here we cannot get rid of the effect by inserting attenuation at the receiving end. The only cures are for the more powerful station's transmitter power to be reduced, for the location of the weaker station's transmitter to be changed, or for the direction of the weaker station's signal to be changed, so that the signals do not hit the same portion of the ionosphere.

Long delay echoes

Occasionally, especially on the higher frequency bands, a station will be heard accompanied by an echo effect with a considerable length of time separating original and echo. This is different to the commonly heard effect when relay stations may be running slightly out of synchronisation; the delay in the case of these *long delay echoes* can be a few seconds or more.

They were first reported before the Second World War, but appear to have become less common since then. Their exact cause is unknown, but they are possibly due to the arrival on the scene of more and more high-power transmitters, which could be having some subtle effect on the ionosphere, reducing the likelihood of LDEs being heard. Other ideas for their course, from the sublime (clouds of ionised gas between the earth and the moon reflecting signals back) to the positively ridiculous (flying saucers!) have been put forward.

F layer anomalies

The F layer gives scientists quite a bit to think about, as there are a few anomalies in its behaviour that are not easily explained in the terms we have discussed in this chapter. For example, F layer ionisation density has been known to show an *increase* during night-time hours, when no ionising radiation reaches the layer from the sun.

Auroral propagation

The aurora borealis, commonly called the Northern Lights, is a phenomenon connected to solar flares. Charged particles generated by a flare get to earth about 24 hours after the radiation caused by the same flare, producing the visual aurora in high latitudes as well as magnetic and ionospheric storms. The aurora itself will occasionally form a reflecting layer or radio signal in the VHF spectrum and also on the higher HF frequencies.

FOURTEEN

Bands

The radio spectrum between 0 and 30 MHz is a pretty crowded place; with amateurs, broadcast stations and utility stations all wanting space. Allocation of frequencies is dealt with by a branch of the United Nations based in Geneva, the *International Telecommunications Union* (ITU). The ITU organises the international telecommunications scene in a series of conferences, which may affect the whole world or just a particular region. ITU *regions* are as follows:

Region 1 Europe, Africa, USSR, Turkey

Region 2 North and South America, Greenland and those parts of the Pacific area which are United States territories, such as Guam

Region 3 Oceania, Australasia and Asia, except for the areas covered in regions 1 and 2.

These regions are further subdivided into *zones*.

The major conferences run by the ITU are called *World Administrative Radio Conferences* (WARC), the last major one of which was in 1979 (WARC-79). The decisions made at these conferences form the *International Table of Frequency Allocations*, which determine how different parts of the spectrum are to be used. Individual countries are allowed to exercise some variation in this, provided their activities do not cause problems for other countries that are sticking to the letter of the law. Decisions made at these conferences are not rapidly taken up; the changes to the size of the broadcast bands agreed at WARC-79 were not actually brought into effect until 1982. These large conferences are not frequent, but there are regular smaller gatherings where particular parts of the frequency spectrum are planned out without large alterations to the frequency allocation tables.

There are differences in frequency use between different regions and countries; for example, 7000 to 7300 kHz is allocated for amateur radio operation in Region 2, but in Regions 1 and 3 only frequencies between 7000 and 7100 are for amateurs; 7100 to 7300 is a broadcast band.

You will find, though, that users of the spectrum do tend to wander a little from their allocated areas; a common problem is the presence in the 7000 to 7100 kHz range of some quite powerful European broadcast stations. Broadcasters also tend to congregate around the edges of broadcast bands, where the interference from other stations is less intense.

The precise frequencies used by broadcasters depends upon the time of year and the state of the sunspot cycle. October and March often sees frequency changes, and as the sunspot count increases the international broadcasters tend to head for the relatively clear higher frequencies, making use of the improved conditions on these bands that accompany high sunspot counts.

A review of the spectrum

It would be a tough job listing *everything* that you can hear between 0 and 30 MHz; that is what books like the WRTH are for. However, the rest of this chapter will give an indication of what you can expect to hear in different parts of the frequency spectrum.

5 kHz to 148 kHz

The VLF section of the spectrum is populated by maritime navigation beacons, time stations and weather stations. Various types of natural phenomena, such as *whistlers*, can be heard at the lower end of this frequency range. Ionospheric disturbances can also be detected by monitoring the atmospherics to be heard in this frequency range, as night-time reception of atmospherics is improved greatly during some types of ionospheric storm. These are called *sudden enhancement of atmospherics* (SEAs). Few receivers go down this far, and if you are interested you will require a converter and a good aerial and earth system.

148 kHz to 285 kHz

The long wave broadcast band is occupied by large, powerful broadcasters from Region 1, but is not allocated as a broadcast band outside this region. High power broadcast stations may have ranges of a few hundred miles both day and night, though reception is better at night than in daylight, and local storms can cause severe interference.

285 kHz to 520 kHz

Occupied by utility stations.

520 kHz to 1620 kHz

The medium wave broadcast band is one we are all likely to be familiar with, occupied as it is by our domestic national and local radio stations. In Region 3, broadcasting is carried out on frequencies as high as 1700 kHz, while in Region 2 the upper limit of the band is 1600 kHz. Channels are 9 kHz apart in Regions 1 and 3, and 10 kHz apart in Region 2, although some stations operate in the gaps between channels. The MW band is known as the AM band in some parts of the world, notably the US.

The ground wave coverage of a typical MW station can be several tens of miles, depending upon the power used and the transmitting aerial. Sky waves are absorbed during the day by the D layer, but as night falls and the D layer disperses the signals reach the E layer and are then received several hundred or even thousands of miles distant. For DX reception, the path between transmitter and receiver should be in darkness. Long distance reception appears to be best in the spring and autumn of low sunspot count years. This is especially true on high latitude signal paths, such as those between the UK and North America. DX reception is also affected by the state of the geomagnetic field; a disturbed field giving poor DX at high latitudes. Funnily enough, there is evidence to suggest that DX paths between the UK and Central and South America are actually *improved* when North American reception is poor! Results in summer are usually poorer than they are in winter, spring or autumn.

In terms of DX, if you are seeking stations to the west of the UK, such as the US and Canada, signals will be greatest around the time corresponding to sunset at the transmitter site and sunrise in the UK – remember that there has to be a path of darkness between the two stations. If you are looking to the east, peaks in signal strength will occur at UK sunset and transmitter sunrise. DX reception is easier at the high frequency end of the MW band, though in all cases a limiting factor is the amount of local QRM caused by European and UK stations. There are two ways around this; use a directional aerial, such as a ferrite rod or loop aerial, or wait until the European stations close down.

Stations on the Eastern seaboard of the US, such as *CJYQ* in Newfoundland (930 kHz), are the easiest DX to hear in the UK, and can act as beacons, indicating whether other stations from that area are likely to be heard. However, all DX on the medium frequencies is prone to slow fading, each fade often taking several minutes. So, patience on all the medium frequency bands is a virtue! In addition, you will often find that poor conditions can last for a few nights.

1800 kHz to 2000 kHz – 160 metres

The next area of activity is 'top band', the lowest frequencies available to amateurs. Not surprisingly, it has much in common with the medium wave broadcast bands. DX reception starts at around sunset when Europe becomes audible. North America comes in when there is a path of darkneses between the UK and US, and South America is usually audible between 0230 hours or so and dawn. The Pacific area is unlikely to be heard at all, due to the fact that a path of darkness between transmitter and receiver is likely to exist for only a very short period of time. Like MW, best reception is around spring, autumn and winter in low sunspot years.

Some countries do not allow amateur operation in this band, and some interference is to be expected from coastal stations. If you can read CW, you are likely to make more 'catches' on 160 metres than if you listen with SSB only. The best time to listen to the band is probably when there is a contest on!

2000 kHz to 2300 kHz

Between 2000 kHz and 2300 kHz there are only utility stations, particularly ship-to-shore radio services.

2300 kHz to 2500 kHz – 120 metres

This broadcast band is the first 'tropical' band, so called because it is only used in the tropical areas of the world. It is used mainly by Region 3 countries, but you will also hear some stations from Central and South America. Low powers are the rule here, mostly less than 1000 watts. There is severe interference from non-broadcast stations, as well as lots of storm static. Propagation on this band is similar to that on MW or 160 metres, although there are fewer stations. On 2500 kHz, there are a few time and frequency standard stations.

A selective set and a notch filter are useful on all the tropical bands; the selectivity can be reduced to cut down noise and minimise adjacent channel interference, and the notch filter is useful to reduce interfering RTTY, CW or heterodynes. A decent aerial is also a must. Bandpass filters at the audio stages of the receiver can be used to limit receiver bandwidth to try to reduce interference.

We are now approaching the HF region of the spectrum, and propagation via the F layer becomes the main mode of long distance propagation, rather than the E layer propagation noted for the MF frequencies previously discussed. The D layer still absorbs signals in the day, but at night long distance reception becomes possible via the F layer.

2500 kHz to 3200 kHz

Occupied by utility stations.

3200 kHz to 3400 kHz – 90 metres

The next band of interest is the 90 metre tropical band, occupied by African, Asian and South American stations, and powers are fairly low. Again, severe interference from storms and RTTY and CW stations will be noted.

3500 kHz to 4000 kHz – 75 and 80 metres

The Region 1, 80 metre amateur band runs from 3500 to 3800 kHz, but is extended to 4000 kHz in Region 2. In Regions 1 and 3, 3950 to 4000 kHz is used for broadcasting. This is significant, as the 75 metre band is the lowest HF band to be occupied by some of the 'big boys', such as the BBC and *Voice of America*.

DX reception on this band is best in winter afternoons and evenings with low sunspot counts, but there is always plenty to hear. Daytime on 80 metres is a good place to start listening to amateurs, as it is the main band for trans-european working on HF. You will always hear plenty of signals at reasonable strength and, as the day progresses and night falls, DX will become apparent. Again, a path of darkness is a requirement for DX to be heard, and lightning static and interference from commercial stations can constitute major problems.

In the amateur band section, the lower portion is reserved for CW and RTTY, with LSB contacts being heard above 3600 kHz. The top portion of the Region 1 band, 3790 to 3800 kHz, is reserved for DX working by a 'gentleman's agreement'. You will often hear split frequency contracts between North America and Europe, as many US amateurs cannot transmit on LSB below 3800 kHz and European stations can not transmit above 3800 kHz! Even in Europe, listening above 3800 kHz will reveal some good catches. With regard to the 75 metre broadcast band, the more powerful European broadcasters will tend to overwhelm the weaker Region 3 stations.

4750 kHz to 5060 kHz – 60 metres

Between 75 metres and 60 metres, the spectrum is occupied by maritime and aeronautical mobile stations – ship-to-shore, etc. At 4750 kHz we get the more popular tropical band stations, occupied by a variety of stations in Regions 1, 2 and 3. Fortunately, there are no European stations in the band, so the fainter DX is more audible. Interference is still experienced from commercial stations, and lightning static can be a problem. DX reception is best in low sunspot years; winter will give good reception over paths of darkness, and spring and autumn will also give reasonable results. In summer, though, do not expect too much DX. Typically, you will hear African stations in the afternoon and evening, and Southern and Central America, Asiatic USSR and China in the late evening and overnight. An easy catch is Africa *Number 1* on 4830 kHz – on odd occasions I have heard this station in early afternoon.

Again, although some medium distance propagation is possible via the E layer, DX signals tend to arrive via F layer propagation. Around 5000 kHz you are likely to hear some of the frequency standard stations, easily recognised by their regular pipping.

5950 kHz to 6200 kHz – 49 metres

If 80 metres is a good amatuer band to start on, then 49 metres must be in the running as the newcomer's broadcast band. Except under highly disturbed conditions, such as SIDs, there are stations audible on 49 metres around the clock. Another band that gives its best performance in low sunspot periods, it is quite possible to hear virtually any part of the world, at night, in winter. Reception in autumn and spring is also quite good and even the summer months may produce stations up to a couple of thousand miles distance.

The big problem on 49 metres is interference from other broadcast stations. The band is heavily used in Europe and so looking for DX signals often relies on you winkling stations out from under or between closer and more powerful stations. There is little problem from lightning static. This is the first band in which receiver overload is likely to be a problem, and so you should take the precautions outlined in Chapter 11, especially if you are using a long aerial.

7000 kHz to 7300 kHz – 40 and 41 metres

Life gets tough here; the first 100 kHz is an amateur band in all Regions, and frequencies between 7100 and 7300 kHz are also available to amateurs in Regions 2 and 3 whilst being earmarked for broadcast use in Region 1. In addition, several European broadcast stations, notably *Radio Tirana*, tend to occupy the 7000 to 7100 kHz slot. All this tends to make listening for amateur DX signals quite difficult.

Looking at Region 1 first, 40 metres is split into 2 sections – 7000 to about 7040 kHz is CW only, and 7040 to 7100 kHz is CW and LSB. In Region 2, the split between CW and LSB is at 7150 kHz, so if you want to hear voice contacts on 40 metres from Region 2, you will have to listen through all the broadcast stations!

In propagation terms, 40 and 41 metres are similar to the 49 metre band, although DX reception is curtailed by the sheer amount of European interference. Again, receiver overload may cause problems.

We are now approaching a change in behaviour; the remaining bands can offer good DX in the daytime, and tend to be better in high sunspot years. Once above about 1500 kHz, reception also declines at night, with bands going dead for hours, particularly in low sunspot years. However, the higher HF bands can be really exciting places, especially when the sunspot count starts climbing. Storm static disappears, to be replaced by local electrical noise and even, between 20 and 30 MHz, radio noise from the sun! The higher frequencies will penetrate the D and E layers, and propagation is via the F layers.

9500 kHz to 9900 kHz – 31 metres

Between the end of the 40 metre band and the beginning of the 31 metre band, there is an awful lot of morse code, SITOR and RTTY on frequencies used by maritime stations. In addition, you will find a few broadcast stations operating outside the recognised band limits; *Radio Beijing* is especially fond of operating in this way! You will find that the 31 metre band tends to spill out from its allocated areas, stations being heard from 9410 to 9988 kHz. This band is a half-way house between the higher bands, which become better in high sunspot years, and the lower frequency bands, which are good mainly in periods of low sunspot count. Reception of signals from Europe is easy in the day, whatever the state of the sunspot cycle, and throughout the darkness hours of much of the year stations several thousand miles away can be heard. The band will occasionally close in the middle of the night, when only reasonably near stations will be heard, particularly in winter. Best times for DX reception are around sunset and sunrise.

The band end is indicated by the presence of frequency standard stations around 10000 kHz.

10100 kHz to 10150 kHz – 30 metres

This amateur band is only available for CW users, and considerable interference from commercial stations is experienced. In propagation terms, it is similar in behaviour to the 31 metre broadcast band, and provides amateur operators with an interest in propagation a useful band of frequencies between the lower HF bands (160, 80 and 40) and the higher bands (20, 15 and 10 metres).

11650 kHz to 12050 kHz – 25 metres

Another good all-day band, especially in periods of high sun spots when it is open for worldwide communication for much of the day. Dawn and dusk are good times to listen, with stations up to a couple of thousand miles away predominating in the morning and afternoon. Come late afternoon and evening, DX reception improves. The main problem here is interference from other broadcast stations.

13600 kHz to 13800 kHz – 22 metres

This band is a relatively new one; WARC-79 added it when it extended the other broadcast bands. Few countries have really taken it up, and often when tuning it all you hear are *Radio Moscow* outlets. Performance would appear to be similar to the 20 metre amateur band.

14000 kHz to 14350 kHz – 20 metres

The 20 metre amateur band is probably *the* DX reception band for amateur operators, offering stations from all over the world for most of the day. It is affected by sunspots to some degree, but even in quiet sun years the band is open from dawn to dusk. In high sunspot years, the only time the band closes is for a couple of hours in the dead of winter nights. Mid-winter is not too good on 20 metres, but it is extremely rare for the band not to be open to all continents during the day.

In the morning, stations from the Middle East and Asia are likely to be heard, followed by European stations, with paths across the Atlantic opening up any time from 0900 hours onwards, depending upon conditions. As the afternoon progresses, stations from Africa and Australasia are likely to be heard, the latter via the short path. Southern and Central America appear in the evening, with good paths to North America.

Most countries allow USB to be used only above 14100 kHz. The band is very popular in contests and is used by DXpeditions. In addition several nets can be heard; it is even possible to hear the US Antarctic survey bases occasionally.

15100 kHz to 15450 kHz – 19 metres

Around 15000 kHz you will hear a few standard frequency stations; an easy one to hear is the Soviet station on 14996 kHz. Between 15000 and 15100 kHz you will hear a few out-of-band broadcasters. High powers are often used on this band – several hundred kilowatts is not rare.

The band is heavily dependant upon sunspots, and in high sunspot count years can give good DX reception performance all day. In low years, reception of stations up to 1500 miles away can be expected, but the band will often close down after dark. The best times to listen are spring and autumn, with good DX reception possibilities in the late afternoon and early evening. DX signals can also be heard after local sunrise. However, stations will be heard after sunset and well into the night, especially in summer when the sunspot count is high. With a long aerial, South American stations are occasionally audible after dark, although you need to take care not to overload your receiver.

17550 kHz to 17900 kHz – 16 metres

Well, most people used to either love or hate this band, due to the amount of jamming that could be heard, but things are now picking up a bit. This band has not got as many European stations in it as the 19 metre band, and in low sunspot years is strictly a 'daylight only' band. The best DX reception periods are likely to be in spring and autumn, though summer will occasionally provide catches from Africa and Asia. The performance of this band generally improves as sunspot count increases.

18068 kHz to 18168 kHz – 16 metre band

This is the second WARC-79 band, though with little activity noted so far. Again, it is a CW-only band, and propagation on the band should be similar to that on the 16 metre broadcast band. At 18080 kHz, you can hear the *BBC World Service*, operating on the principle that 'we were here first'!

20000 kHz

Yet another frequency standard slot, the principle station here being *WWV*.

21000 kHz to 21450 kHz – 15 metres

This is again heavily dependant on sunspots, with high counts giving very good signal strengths. The band is likely to close for just a couple of hours in the dead of night in high count years, and worldwide reception is likely to be experienced, starting with the far east as the band opens, and on-going reception areas moving east-to-west as the day progresses.

In low count years, reception is very poor, with the best DX signals from North American stations, heard in the afternoon, and some South American stations. North/south paths are often better than east/west paths on this band.

21450 kHz to 21850 kHz – 13 metres

This broadcast band is similar in performance to the 15 metre amateur band. DX reception is possible in daylight, with early spring and late autumn giving the best results. Performance improves in high sunspot count years. Even in poor years, stations from the Middle East, Europe and North Africa can be heard. In good years, world-wide reception is possible, but in poor years relatively few stations will be heard.

Between 21850 and 24890 kHz, the spectrum is reserved for utility stations, but these frequencies only become occupied in good sunspot years.

24890 kHz to 24990 kHz – 12 metres

The final WARC-79 band, this has seen almost no activity since its release. However, it is likely to behave in a similar way to the 11 metre broadcast band. Again, this band is for CW users only.

25600 kHz to 26100 kHz – 11 metres

In periods of high sunspot counts, this band gives excellent results. However, when sunspots are few, virtually no stations are heard, mainly because the broadcasters leave the band for the more reliable lower frequencies.

28000 kHz to 29700 kHz – 10 metres

The 10 metre amateur band can be quite amazing in high sunspot years, when stations from all continents can be heard in a matter of minutes with very simple aerials, although the band usually closes around midnight until the following day. In poor conditions, little can be heard, and during the periods of few sunspots the band is quiet. Whether this is due to poor propagation or whether it is due to amateurs shunning the band for lower frequencies is a matter for debate!

The band is CW only between 28000 and 28200 kHz, the rest of the band being available for telephony. A popular slot for DX stations is between 28400 to 28700 kHz.

Of course, if SWLing were as predictable as this, it would not be all that interesting! You will find that stations appear at times and on frequencies they should not do, and this is one of the reasons that the hobby is so popular – no one is ever 100% sure about what they are going to hear next!

FIFTEEN

Using computers in SWL

With the advent of cheap home computers, many listeners and amateurs have started using them to help out in their hobby. In this chapter, I will give a quick review of how the machines can be used. It is really aimed at listeners who have got a little knowledge of computers; enough, say, to write their own small programs in BASIC. In general terms, computers can be used in three main ways.

First, circuit design. Programs exist to allow circuits to be 'tested' without actually building them! These circuit analysis packages are quite expensive, but you can write simple programs yourself to help with the calculations involved in circuit design.

Second is to aid signal reception. The computer can be interfaced to a radio receiver and programmed to decode CW, RTTY or AMTOR signals. A terminal unit of some description is needed, although some listeners have had success by just connecting the headphone output of the receiver to the tape-recorder input of the computer! Suitable programs are required to make the computer do this, and there are several commercially available packages to choose from. Alternatively, CW and RTTY decoders are fairly straightforward programming projects.

Finally, computers may be used to aid in administrative tasks. They can be used for a variety of 'housekeeping' jobs around the shack, from printing out log sheets to keeping the whole listening log on a computer database! Programs can be written to generate random morse, calculate bearings and distances, and a whole host of similar jobs.

Having seen some of the areas in which a computer can be *useful*, let us start by looking at the biggest *drawback* that the computer has when used in the SWLs shack; interference!

Computer radio noise

Computers work by shuffling around, at high speed, 5 V and 0 V pulses which represent numbers. These pulses generate a great forest of harmonics throughout the radio spectrum, often up to several hundred megahertz! In addition, various circuits within computers may generate signals on spot frequencies, say, 1 MHz signals caused by the internal clock of the computer and 18 MHz signals from parts of the computer responsible for its graphics images. Not all computers produce the same amount of interference, though. In addition to interference caused by the computer itself, peripheral equipment can also cause problems. A computer display, be it portable TV or proper monitor, is likely to generate signals like TV time base interference. Disc drives and printers are possible culprits too – I once spent a great deal of time blaming my BBC microcomputer for some interference which was eventually traced back to my printer!

You will also find the amount of interference generated by the computer system varies, depending upon what the machine is doing. Interference is often worse when a program is running or when, for example, discs are being read or written to or documents printed. The first thing we must do before considering using the computer in the shack is to consider ways in which computer-generated interference can be minimised. The interference travels by three main routes: radiation, where noise signals are radiated as radio waves by the computer system; direct injection, where noise signals travel into the radio system via the mains wiring of the house or any other direct connection between the receiver and computer system; and a combination of the two, where signals are injected into the mains wiring of the house and then radiated, the house wiring acting as an aerial.

Proximity of computer – radiation

Position the computer and its associated peripherals as far away from the receiver *and* any aerial input leads to the receiver as possible. This limits interference due to direct radiation of noise signals from the computer circuits.

Type of aerial – radiation

An external aerial, connected to the receiver by a length of co-axial cable, is almost essential if you are going to be running programs whilst listening. Internal aerials will pick up a great deal of interference from the computer system. An ATU will help here.

Mains wiring – radiation/injection

If possible, plug the computer and its peripherals into a different mains socket to that used by the receiver – some listeners may use 4-way distribution blocks for their gear. Resist the temptation to plug the computer into a spare socket on this. Plugging the two devices into different sockets, preferably on different ring mains, will help reduce this effect.

Further improvement can be obtained with low pass filters, like those shown in Chapter 12. Commercial devices can be obtained which filter out all frequencies above 100 kHz or so, and it is useful to connect your computer to the mains via one of these, as interference onto mains wiring is prevented. On the other hand, connecting the receiver to the mains via such a filter will prevent direct injection of noise *from* the mains, but will not prevent the receiver picking up noise injected into the mains by the computer and then *radiated* by the mains. Ideally, if you can afford it, a filter at the mains input of both receiver and computer will minimise this interference.

Screening of equipment – radiation

Most home computers for UK consumption come in plastic cases with no attempt to provide screening to prevent the leakage of RF from the computer. In some cases, it is possible to purchase metal cases for particular brands of computers. Alternatively, you can try the expedients of lining the case with aluminium foil, glued in, or spraying the inside of the case with conductive paint. In either method, this conductive screen should be earthed. Take care to avoid short circuits between the screen and the circuit board; if you are not sure about this, get experienced help! In addition, if you plan to use paint, first check it will not attack the plastic of the case.

In a similar way, a well-screened receiver will help prevent interference signals of this sort being picked up by the receiver's IF strip and RF stages.

Direct connection between receiver and computer – injection

When we connect a terminal unit between receiver and computer

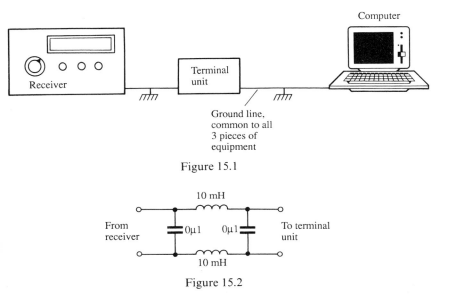

Figure 15.1

Figure 15.2

(Figure 15.1), there is likely to be a direct link between computer and receiver via the 0 V line of each piece of equipment, on which interference may be carried. A first step to minimise interference is by connecting a low pass filter between terminal unit and computer, and possibly terminal unit and receiver. The easiest, and one of the most effective ways of doing this is to wrap the leads linking the equipment a few times around a ferrite rod, thus forming an inductor. This may give surprisingly good results! A similar treatment can be given to the mains lead of the receiver and computer.

Alternatively, low pass filters can be built from discrete components (Figure 15.2). If interference is very persistent, then you may need to consider using an opto-isolator circuit, which electrically isolates terminal unit and computer by using a beam of light to relay the digital signals to the computer input. A simple opto-isolator circuit is shown in Figure 15.3.

Computer applications

Anyone seriously interested in computer software for SWL and amateur purposes should really get the 'Bible' of the field, *Amateur*

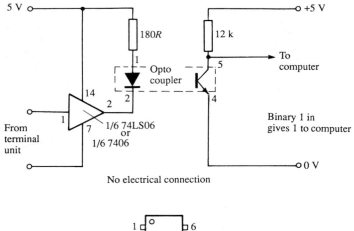

Figure 15.3

Radio Software by John Morris, *GM4ANB*, published by the RSGB. Great stuff, with lots of listings and useful programs.

We will start by examining the 'admin' jobs that a computer can be called upon to do in the shack.

Log keeping

A simple computer database program, which allows your computer to behave like an electronic filing cabinet, can be used to store log entries. Commercial packages exist to do this. The advantage of a computer log over the standard paper log is that it is easier to search through the computer log for different pieces of information. For example, you could ask for a list of all the occasions on which you logged *Radio Australia* in the last six months. In addition, whereas standard logs are organised in date and time order, a good database program will allow you to list out the log entries in any order you want – callsign, frequency, date and time, etc. The system I use, which runs on my

Amstrad PC computer, allows me to do this quite easily, and also does other jobs, like prefix counting, automatically.

The disadvantage of some systems is that they can be slow when there is a large quantity of information stored. Also, the computer needs to be constantly up-and-running during a listening session, for convenient loggings. There is always a risk of data loss, too, especially if the information is stored on cassette tape, and so it becomes necessary to make regular and frequent back-up copies of all information.

If you are still using a paper log (and I admit that I use both computer and paper-based systems) the computer can still help out by printing log sheets, with pre-printed headings. Listing 1 is of a simple program for the BBC microcomputer, which does this.

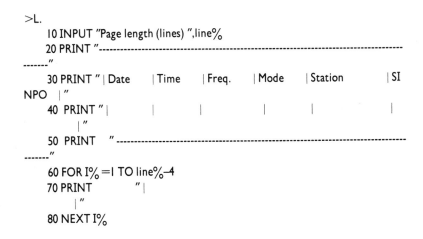

```
>L.
    10 INPUT "Page length (lines) ",line%
    20 PRINT "----------------------------------------------------------------
-------"
    30 PRINT " | Date     | Time    | Freq.    | Mode     | Station      | SI
NPO  | "
    40 PRINT " |          |         |          |          |              |
      | "
    50 PRINT    " ----------------------------------------------------------------
-------"
    60 FOR I% =1 TO line%-4
    70 PRINT        " |
      | "
    80 NEXT I%
```

Listing 1 A program for the BBC microcomputer to print log sheets

Circuit design

Although we are not likely to sit down and write a circuit analysis program, I have found it quite useful to have a few small programs available if I need to build, say, a low pass filter. A simple program for selecting component values for a low pass filter is given in Listing 2.

>L.

```
 10 REM Simple RC filter calculator. Will work for any
 20 REM RC filter design. Written on BBC Microcomputer
 30 :
 40 PRINT "Enter 0 for the value you require"
 50 PRINT "E.g. To calculate resistance required"
 60 PRINT "enter frequency and capacitance and enter"
 70 PRINT "0 for the resistance value"
 80 PRINT:PRINT
 90 INPUT "Cut off frequency (Hz)      ",freq
100 INPUT "Resistor Value (Ohms)    ",R
110 INPUT "Capacitor Value (F)        ",C
120 :
130 REM now select which calculation we require
140 :
150 IF freq =0 THEN GOSUB 290
160 IF R =0 THEN GOSUB 310
170 IF C =0 THEN GOSUB 330
180 PRINT:PRINT
190 :
200 REM Whatever we did, now print the results
210 :
220 PRINT "Resistance is:  ";R;" ohms"
230 PRINT "Capacitance is   ";C;" farads"
240 PRINT "Frequency is      ";freq; " Hertz"
250 END
260 :
270 REM here are all the subroutines
280 :
290 freq =1/(6.28*R*C)
300 RETURN
310 R =1/(6.28*C*freq)
320 RETURN
330 C =1/(6.28*R*freq)
340 RETURN
```

Listing 2 A program to select low pass filter component value

QSL card production

With the advent of cheap graphics programs, it is possible to use the computer to print out QSL cards if you are an amateur, or listener cards if you are an SWL. A simple card produced in this way is shown in Figure 15.4. Some operators have a dislike of computer-produced QSL cards, saying that they are too easily forged, but very good results are possible.

G1UQW   Sheffield
ENGLAND

Locator: I093FJ

Date	Time	Band	Mode

Your signals   :
My station   :
73s from   :

Figure 15.4

Listeners attempting to get QSLs out of broadcast stations may note I have had some success with a computer printed report sheet; which, after listening, I fill in with relevant details.

Learning CW

Although electronic random morse generators are available, and there is a vast amount of practice material on the air, there is a need in the early stages for a means of generating CW characters at varying rates. Listing 3 is of a simple program to generate random morse code. The REM statements in the program indicate the function of different parts of the code. The program is written for use on the BBC micro but is easily transferred on to other computers.

```
>
>L.
     10 INPUT "Enter a dit length ",dit%
     20 INPUT "Number of letters in group ",group%
     30 INPUT "Enter a gap length ",gap%
     40 S$ =""
```

```
 50 FOR Z%=1 TO group%
 60 K%=RND (26) :RESTORE 170:FOR I%=1 TO K%:READ A$:NEXT:
    RESTORE 180:FOR I%=1 TO K%:READ B$:NEXT
 70 FOR J%=1 TO LEN(B$)
 80 IF MID$(B$,J%,1)="." THEN SOUND 1,-12,100,dit%
 90 IF MID$(B$,J%,1)="-" THEN SOUND 1,-12,100,dit%*3
100 SOUND 1,0,100,dit%
110 NEXT
120 FOR G%=1 TO gap%:SOUND 1,0,100,dit%:NEXT G%
130 S$=S$+A$
140 NEXT Z%
150 INPUT "What was the morse",A$:PRINT "It was "+S$
160 GOTO 40
170 DATA A,B,C,D,E,F,G,H,I,J,K,L,M,N,O,P,Q,R,S,T,U,V,W,X,Y,Z
180 DATA .—,—...,—.—.,—..,.,..—.,——.,....,..,.——,
    —.—,.—..,——,—.,———,.——.,——.—,.—.,...,—,..—,
    ...—,.——,—..—,—.——,——..
```

Listing 3 A program to generate random morse code.

Test equipment

Computers, with devices called *analogue-to-digital converters* allow us to use them as voltmeters, resistance meters, ammeters and a host of other functions. Computers can measure frequency and time periods, generate test signals, and so on. All this requires software and usually some hardware to interface the computer to the circuit under test, but can prove to be a great money saver is a suitable computer is already available.

Computerised reception of signals

The computer has made RTTY available to a vast number of people whose wives, husbands or parents would have objected to the traditional gear needed to decode this mode; a large, clanking, mechanical teleprinter! In addition, CW can now be read by anyone: knowledge of the code used is unnecessary.

It is not possible in the space available to go into details about modes such as AMTOR, SSTV or ASCII. But, a simple algorithm for decoding RTTY and a simple program for decoding morse are certainly possible. A few general points first, though.

1 an input port is required on the computer, to allow connection of your terminal unit

2 reasonable results for CW can be obtained by writing the programs in BASIC, but for RTTY decoding I have found that machine code is necessary

3 be prepared to experiment with the software, particularly with the CW software, as the program does not take into account variations in sending speed. The RSGB book, *Amateur Radio Software*, gives several CW decoding programs that are self-adjusting in terms of speed.

An RTTY decoding algorithm

A RTTY signal is sent as two tones, called the *mark* and *space* tones. Amateurs use an audio tone of 1445 Hz to indicate a mark and 1275 Hz to indicate a space. A terminal unit is used to convert these audio tones into digital signals, a 5 V pulse at the terminal unit output corresponds to a mark and 0 V corresponds to a space.

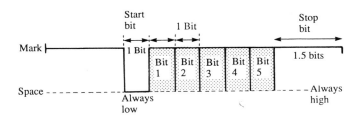

Figure 15.5

The signal is always transmitted in 5-bit words (Figure 15.5), with a prefixed start bit and a suffixed stop bit. The start bit is always low (a space), and the stop bit is always high (a mark). For a 45 baud signal of the type used by amateurs, each date bit and the start bit is 22 ms long, with the stop bit being 33 ms long.

The algorithm for decoding this signal is fairly simple; we read the incoming pulses, convert them to a number representing a character, then use a table of characters to get the one we want to print.

```
REPEAT
REPEAT
  character = 0
  wait for a space
  wait for 11 ms              ; middle of start pulse
UNTIL a space is found        ; ensures we have got a proper
                              ; start signal

wait for 22 ms                ; into 1st bit
IF mark THEN character  =  character + 1
wait for 22 ms                ; into 2nd bit
IF mark THEN character  =  character + 2
wait for 22 ms
IF mark THEN character  =  character + 4
wait for 22 ms
IF mark THEN character  =  character + 8
wait for 22 ms
IF mark THEN character  =  character + 16
; character now holds a number between 0 and
; 32 representing a character in the RTTY
; code. This can be processed as described below
process the character
UNTIL FALSE                   ; go round again for next character
```

Once the character code has been obtained, you can use it to look-up a character in a table of RTTY characters (Table 15.1). You will note that there are two possible interpretations on most RTTY character codes, depending on whether a *letters shift* character or a *figures shift* character has been received. When we start, we assume that we are in *letters shift* mode and so use that column. However, if a *figures shift* character is received (character 27) then we need to use characters from that column until a *letters shift* character (31) is received.

CW decoding

Decoding of a CW signal is a much more difficult proposition because timing of the signal varies depending upon the sender. We *should* be able to rely on the following points, though:

1 a *dit* is the shortest time unit needed

2 a *dah* is three times the length of a dit

Table 15.1 RTTY code character table

Code	Letter shifted	Figure shifted
0	BLANK	BLANK
1	E	3
2	LINE FEED	LINE FEED
3	A	−
4	SPACE	SPACE
5	S	'
6	I	8
7	U	7
8	CARRIAGE RETURN	CARRIAGE RETURN
9	D	$
10	R	4
11	J	BELL SOUND
12	N	,
13	F	!
14	C	:
15	K	(
16	T	5
17	Z	+
18	L	)
19	W	2
20	H	
21	Y	6
22	P	0
23	Q	1
24	O	9
25	B	?
26	G	&
27	FIGURE SHIFT	FIGURE SHIFT
28	M	.
29	X	/
30	V	=
31	LETTERS SHIFT	LETTERS SHIFT

3 the gap between *dits* and *dahs* in a single letter is equivalent to a dit

4 the gap between letters is equivalent to a *dah*.

Listing 4 is of a simple morse code decoding program which will accurately decode morse, though it needs to be 'tweaked' for different sending speeds. You might like to try modifying the program to cope with morse of a varying speed. It was written for a **BBC** microcomputer, which has a user port at address &FE60 in its memory map. Integer variables were used because the BBC microcomputer processes these variables more quickly than other variable types. Users of other computers should be able to modify the program to suit.

In use, simply tune to a strong CW signal and run the program. If garbage is seen on the screen, simply adjust the dit%, gap%, and letter% variables; dit% is the *dit* length, gap% is the inter-element gap length within each character and letter% is the gap between letters in a word.

In this chapter, I have really only scratched the surface of computers in SWLing. It is a field ripe for experimentation but take care; computing can be as addictive as listening!

L.

```
 10 ?&FE62 =0
 20 DIM letter$(66),D%(5)
 30 FOR I% =1 TO 64:READ letter$(I%):NEXT I%
 40 FOR I% =1 TO 5:READ D%(I%):NEXT I%
 50 dit% =50
 60 gap% =50
 70 letter% =160
 80 :
 90 REM start line here
100 :
110 REPEAT UNTIL (?&FE60 AND 1) =0
120 REM wait for input connected to Terminal
130 REM unit to go to '0'
140 :
150 C% =0 : REM character code being built up
160 P% =1 : REM initialise pointer to power of 2 table
170 REM loop back here for decoding a character
180 IF P% <5 D% =D%(P%):(P% =P% +1 : REM pick up next power of two if character
190 REM                              : will be a legal one. Otherwise don't bother
```

```
200 REPEAT UNTIL (?&FE60 AND 1) =1 : REM wait until a '1' is detected
210 REM                          : a dit or dah is being received.
220 T% =0                        : REM initialise counter to 0
230 REPEAT T% =T% +1:UNTIL (?&FE60 AND 1) =0    : REM count while dit or dah is
240 REM                                         : being received. i.e. whilst input
250 REM                                         : is equal to '1'
260 IF T% >dit% C% =C% +D%*2 ELSE C% =C% +D%: REM if T% is more than the dit
270 REM                                      : length then we count it as a dah
280 REM                                      : and add D%*2 to the character
290 REM                                      : code being assembled. Otherwise
300 REM                                      : just add D%. This process will
310 REM                                      : eventually give a code in the
320 REM                                      : range 0 to 63
330 T% =0                                    : REM reinitialise counter
340 IF T% >letter% THEN GOSUB 450:PRINT " "; : GOTO 150
350 REM if it's the end of a word, print the letter and a space and go around
360 REM again to pick up the next letter.
370 T% =T% +1 : REM increment counter
380 IF (?&FE60 AND 1) =0 THEN GOTO 340: REM if we're still receiving a 'gap'
390 REM                                : then go around again until a dit or
400 REM                                : dah is received
410 IF T% >gap% THEN GOTO 430          : REM if end of letter, go and print it
420 GOTO 170                           : REM otherwise get next dit or dah
430 GOSUB 450
440 GOTO 150
450 REM subroutine to print character held in C%
460 IF C% <65 PRINT letter$(C%); ELSE PRING "—"; : REM print '—' if out of range
470 T% =0
480 RETURN
490 DATA e,t,i,n,a,m,s,d,r,g,u,k,w,o,h,b,l,z,f,c,p,—,v,x,—,q,y,—,j,—,5,6,—,7,—,
—,—,8,—,—,—,—,—,—,—,9,4,—,—,—,—,——,—,—,3,—,—,—,2,—,1,0,—,—
500 DATA 1,2,4,8,16
```

Listing 4 A morse code decoding program

Appendix 1

Useful addresses

Maplin Electronic Supplies.
One of the companies I used for components in the circuits shown in the text. Good catalogue, too.

Maplin Electronic Supplies,
PO Box 3,
Rayleigh,
Essex

Rapid Electronics.
Another component stockist.

Rapid Electronics,
Hill Farm Industrial Estate,
Boxted,
Colchester,
Essex CO4 5RD

Magenta Electronics.
Yet another stockist!

Magenta Electronics Limited,
135 Hunter Street,
Burton on Trent,
Staffordshire DE14 2ST

Cirkit.
Still another component stockist.

Cirkit,
Park Lane,
Broxbourne,
Herts EN10 7NQ

Electromail.
Another component stockist!
Good catalogue; supplier of RS Components components.

Electromail,
PO Box 33,
Corby,
Northants NN17 9EL

Radio Society of Great Britain,
Lambda House,
Cranborne Road,
Potters Bar,
Hertfordshire EN6 3JE

International Short Wave League '87,
10 Clyde Crescent,
Wharton,
Winsford,
Cheshire CW7 3LA

Department of Trade and Industry,
Radiocommunications Division,
Waterloo Bridge House,
Waterloo Bridge Road,
London SE1 8UA

Technical Software.
A supplier of computer software for listening.

Technical Software,
Fron,
Upper Llandwrog,
Caernarfon LL54 7RF

Interbooks.
A useful supplier of books on radio listening.

Interbooks,
Stanley,
Perth,
Scotland PH1 4QQ

Appendix 2

Becoming a radio amateur

If you wish to transmit on VHF and short wave bands, you need to pass the Radio Amateurs Examination (RAE). Details of the examination are available from the Department of Trade and Industry but, briefly, the examination consists of two parts; a written examination and a 12 words per minute morse code test. The written examination is set by the City and Guilds Institute, and is in two parts, one on licensing and interference matters and the second paper is on radio theory, practice and operating procedures. The written papers are both multiple choice, that is, a question is posed with, say, five options for answers, one of which is correct. Once both these written papers are passed, you can get a *B* licence which allows you to use frequencies of 50 MHz and above. To get the 'full ticket', or *A* licence, which permits operation on any of the amateur bands, the morse test must be passed. This is now run by the RSGB, which supplies details of the next round of morse tests in *Radio Communications*, each month.

Appendix 3

Further reading

Foundations of Wireless and Electronics, MG Scroggie, Newnes Technical Books. Good introduction to elementary radio.

World Radio and TV Handbook, Billboard Publications. Published annually. Invaluable guide to what's on where.

The Complete Shortwave Listener's Handbook. 3rd Edition, Bennet, Helms, Hardy, Tab Books. Interesting review of listening techniques, but from a US standpoint.

Radio Amateur and Listener's Pocket Book, Steve Money, G3FZX. Heinemann Professional Publishing. Useful data on listening matters.

Short Wave Radio Listener's Handbook, Arthur Miller, Patrick Stephens Limited. Useful introduction to SWLing, more emphasis on amateur operation than broadcast band listening.

A Guide to Amateur Radio, 19th Edition, Pat Hawker, G3VA. Published by the RSGB. Very good introduction to the world of amateur radio.

Amateur Radio Operating Manual, Third Edition. Edited by RJ Eckersley, published by the RSGB. Guide to practical operating on the amateur bands; useful stuff for listeners as well, though.

Radio Communications Handbook, Fifth Edition. Published by the RSGB. The book for technically-minded amateurs and listeners. Good and meaty, with receivers and transmitters detailed.

Radio Communications Handbook. Published by the American Radio Relay League (ARRL). US equivalent of the last book. Very useful, available from the RSGB.

Amateur Radio Software, J. Morris, published by the RSGB. Excellent source of programs and ideas for computer users.

Radio Wave Propagation (HF Bands), FC Judd. Published by Heinemann Newnes. Good study of propagation.

Many other books of interest are found in local libraries or good bookshops. In addition, a catalogue is available from 'Interbooks' (see Appendix 1). The RSGB also publishes several other books of interest. In addition, keep an eye on radio and electronic press for up-to-date information on frequencies in use, equipment reviews, etc.

Index